Love Notes to Our Moms

AND OTHER WOMEN OF INFLUENCE

Speaking of
Women's Health™
Be Strong • Be Healthy • Be in Charge

THE BOOK   VOLUME V

She is the center of your first memories of childhood. Maybe your first memory is of her listening to your stories about the first day of school, or perhaps it's of her racing along side you as you peddled the wheels on your bicycle for the first time. Whether it's the warmth of her hugs, the smell of her perfume or her stories about work, she's the reason Speaking of Women's Health has collected *Love Notes to Our Moms and Other Women of Influence*.

For many, the woman in our loving memories is our Mother. Or, maybe *she* is the Grandmother who raised you, or a lady in the neighborhood who cared deeply about you. All of these women represent the best the world has to offer. In this book, you'll find love letters from incredibly successful women to their Mothers and other influential women who helped shape them into who they are today.

Each of the letters is as unique and special as the women who wrote them. Speaking of Women's

Health is proud to share these letters with you and showcase women who live our motto: "Be Strong • Be Healthy • Be in Charge." We extend a heartfelt "thank you" to each of these women for sharing their love notes and favorite family recipes... and to the chef at Canyon Ranch who modified some of these recipes to make them healthier – and still delicious! While we recognize that some of these family favorites are not suitable for a makeover by Canyon Ranch; nonetheless, some of these family favorites are food for the soul. Enjoy them on special occasions with no regrets!

In Speaking of Women's Health tradition, this book offers you tips and tidbits on an array of topics from baby care to menopause, from exercise to nutrition, and from allergies to heart disease. We want to empower and educate you to "make informed decisions about the health, well-being and personal safety" for you and your family.

Speaking of Women's Health encourages you to read through the book and then write your own personal love note to your Mom or to another woman who has inspired and encouraged you to live your best life. We have even saved a dedication page, so you can write your letter in *Love Notes to Our Moms and Other Women of Influence* and then give this book to her.

Warm wishes to you and your loved ones,

Dianne

Dianne Dunkelman
Founder & CEO, Speaking of Women's Health

We are **trusted.**
We are **fun!**
We are

Speaking of Women's Health™
Be Strong • Be Healthy • Be in Charge

Love Notes to Our Moms and Other Women of Influence is the 5th in a series of books we've written for women nationwide and just one of the ways we spread our mission of "educating women to make informed decisions about their health, well-being and personal safety."

Since 1996, Speaking of Women's Health has been educating and empowering women nationwide through more than 50 conferences and events across the country. In addition to our Speaking of Women's Health conferences, we have created Universal Sisters™ for African-American women and Hablando de la Salud de la Mujer™ for Hispanic women. We host two in-store events at Wal-Mart stores nationwide – and have free health brochures in Wal-Mart stores every day. We also produce a free quarterly newsletter and a television show, "Lifetime's Speaking of Women's Health" on Lifetime's Real Women Network.

Through our Web site, www.speakingofwomenshealth.com, you can find health information on topics from healthy eating, to exercise and personal safety – to name a few! You'll also find videos on a variety of women's health topics, as well as healthy and delicious recipes.

The nutritional analysis provided is not intended for medical nutritional therapy. If you are following a strict diet for medical or dietary reasons, consult first with a physician or dietitian before planning your meals.

This book is designed to provide information about health, not medical advice.
Please consult your physician if you have any questions or concerns.

Speaking of Women's Health's "Love Notes to Our Moms and Other Women of Influence" is meant to increase your knowledge of current developments in women's health. In no way, however, are any of the suggestions in this book meant to take the place of advice given by your licensed health care professionals. Consult your physician or other licensed health care professional before commencing any medical treatment or exercise program. Speaking of Women's Health doesn't make any claims or endorsements for any products, services or procedures that appear in this book.

Dearest Mother,

Florence Henderson is...

I hope the mail service is better in Heaven than it is down here! I'm so glad Speaking of Women's Health gave me this opportunity to write to you. I think of you so often and now I will try to put into words some of the things I think about.

First, thank you for giving birth to me. Being your tenth child and knowing how many struggles and challenges you faced, I'm very grateful for the gift of life you gave me.

Thanks so much for realizing that I was born singing and for making me do it (yes, you were a "Stage Mother" before the term was created!). You loved music and could play many instruments by ear. I'm sorry you never had the chance to study. You would have been a contender.

Thanks for teaching me that although we were very poor in material things, we could be rich in spirit! You taught me to be honest, to be truthful and to be independent. Your ability to survive so many challenges in your life has often given me the strength to face the challenges in my own life. You kept the faith, you forged ahead – you always had the courage to be you!

And even though I had my moments of resentment and frustration, my respect, admiration and love for you grows stronger everyday. I am proud to be your child!

...known worldwide as Carol Brady, everybody's favorite Mom

Love always,

Roquefort Pear Salad

What a beautiful salad filled with lettuce and pears (antioxidants), walnuts (Omega-3s) and blue cheese (a bit of calcium and lots of taste)!

INGREDIENTS

Salad

2 Tbsp.	pecans, chopped
2 Tbsp.	sugar
3 cups	green leaf lettuce
3	Bartlett pears, cored and chopped
1 1/2 oz.	crumbled Roquefort cheese
1/2	avocado, peeled, pitted and diced
1/2 cup	green onions, thinly sliced

Dressing

3 Tbsp.	red wine vinegar
1 1/2 tsp.	sugar
1 1/2 tsp.	prepared mustard
1 clove	garlic, minced
1/2 tsp.	salt
pinch	black pepper

Cook's Note:
This salad is best when served well tossed. Rather than layering the ingredients, feel free to toss and serve individual salads.

PREPARATION

- Blend ingredients for dressing in a blender and set aside.
- In a skillet, over medium heat, cook pecans with 2 Tbsp. sugar. Continue stirring gently until sugar has melted and caramelized the pecans. Carefully transfer nuts onto waxed paper and allow to cool. Break apart the cooled candied nuts into small pieces.
- In a large serving bowl, layer lettuce, pears, cheese crumbles, avocado and green onion.
- Pour the dressing over the salad and top with the pecan pieces.

NUTRITIONAL ANALYSIS
Makes 6 servings. Each serving contains approximately:

135	calories
3 g.	protein
20 g.	carbohydrates
6 g.	fat
6 mg.	cholesterol
302 mg.	sodium
4 g.	fiber

DEDICATION TO A WOMAN
IN YOUR LIFE

You may choose to use this book as a gift... and, if so, this page has been reserved for you to write your own "Love Note."

_____

_____

_____

_____

_____

_____

_____

_____

_____

_____

_____

_____

_____

_____

_____

_____

_____

CANYONRANCH.

It's an honor and privilege to be associated with the significant work and teachings of Speaking of Women's Health. For more than a decade, Canyon Ranch has supported the Speaking of Women's Health initiative, which so closely mirrors our own mission – health education and responsibility.

This book represents one of the many amazing take-home experiences Speaking of Women's Health provides to women throughout the country, in all walks of life. The importance of taking care of yourself and your family resonates with women who are Mothers, sisters, daughters and caretakers. Canyon Ranch begins by offering our message of integrative health – fitness, nutrition and life management – to our guests, and extends its reach to those who are unable to visit our destination resorts, but still want to embrace a feeling of well-being.

This special-edition Speaking of Women's Health book, *Love Notes to Our Moms and Other Women of Influence*, featuring recipe makeovers by Canyon Ranch Corporate Chef Scott Uehlein, blends the tradition that sometimes accompanies foods with the desire to be healthy. Family favorites that don't meet today's nutritional standards for good health – due to the presence of added fats or calories – don't need to be tossed aside and substituted with new recipes. Sure, there are new spins on old family treats, but foods are so personally associated with people, holidays, feelings and traditions, that we want to preserve. Starting from scratch isn't always necessary, but "tweaking" the old standards to become more healthful is, in order to optimize longevity and avoid disease.

Fortunately, my upbringing allowed for the infusion of fresh, whole fruits and vegetables. My Mother never opened a can of anything (unless she had canned it herself), but served wonderfully prepared fresh or frozen produce, meats and even homemade desserts. I became so spoiled that I didn't really like the taste of cooked vegetables – so much so that I often enlisted help from my anxious brothers to eat what remained on my plate while my parents were otherwise distracted!

I inherited my Mother's love of cooking from scratch and entertaining for friends and family – and I still employ fresh fruits and vegetables in recipes whenever possible. In more than two decades at Canyon Ranch, I have learned much about healthy food choices and preparation and have passed it onto my children and grandchildren.

And that's what it's all about. Traditions. Family. Good Health. Cooking nutritiously can allow you to enjoy all three. Learn how to take your favorite recipes – and make the BEST of them.

Yours in good health,

Roxanne

Roxanne Housley
Canyon Ranch Vice President of Sales & Strategic Alliances

The original "Supremes"...
Florence Ballard,
Mary Wilson
and Diana Ross...
the "Dream" team

Mary and her "Supreme" daughter,
Turkessa, and granddaughter, Mia

Mary and her Mother, Johnnie Mae

My Mom, Johnnie Mae, was an angel. She was one of those human beings who lived by her word. Some parents say "Do as I say, not as I do," but Mom was a different kind of person. Johnnie Mae could not read nor write, she was wise and you could always see the truth in her eyes. Even when Mom was upset, she was gentle; I never heard her say a bad thing about any one. How I got so lucky I cannot begin to tell you. I always tried to do the right things for her. I did not always make it. I wanted to please her because she always made me feel safe.

One of the most painful things to see was Mom trying to learn how to read and write, but, unfortunately, she never learned how. I have a Bible that has her signature on every single page; she never stopped trying. One of her biggest dreams was to see her children go to college. When I decided to sing and not go to college, it broke her heart, but she gave me her blessings anyway. Boy, was I glad when we became famous! One of the first things I did was to buy her a house on the upper east side of Detroit, Michigan. It was the proudest moment of my life. She was very proud of me, I could tell. I know that I had made her very happy. Whenever she came to my shows, her eyes would beam. She was a simple woman with simple desires, and I know that I was blessed to have an angel named Johnnie Mae as my Mother.

At the age of 59 in 2001, I graduated from New York University receiving my associate's degree. I spent five years there and loved every minute of it. My Mother's dream had become my dream, and I made it come true for her and me. I am forever grateful to her for inspiring me even now when I know she is in Heaven. Her essence is with me in every thing I do.

FINANCIAL NOTES

Growing up, most of us received a weekly allowance.

This was Mom's way of teaching us that financial rewards come from fulfilled responsibilities. Empower yourself and be smart about your piggy bank. Spend, contribute and save... investing to ensure your "fiscally-healthy" future.

Planning

1. Begin financial planning now. Don't wait until the perfect moment. Plan for now and modify when your situation changes.

2. Know your net worth. This is a full picture of what you owe and what you own and is a way to measure your financial health. Re-evaluate at least once a year.

3. Discuss your financial goals with your partner. Decide which goals you both share and how you'd fund them. Then list your individual goals and plan how to achieve them.

4. Building wealth is a team sport... Create a financial team with you as the "coach." Bankers, financial planners, lawyers, accountants and insurance people can help you make your plan; however, you set the direction and must always be the decision maker.

5. Make an estate plan. Have emergency information available on where to find documents and important contacts. Create a will and name a guardian for your children. Be sure to sign a living will, a health care proxy and a durable power of attorney.

6. Have an emergency fund. Having money available for six months' worth of fixed expenses relieves the anxiety of living paycheck to paycheck.

Strategy

1. Make sure your investments fit your goals. Don't invest in the stock market for a goal that is only a few years away. Likewise, don't keep long-term funds in an account where you will earn very little.

2. Take advantage of all financial opportunities your company offers. Review your options with an employee benefits representative.

3. Begin a retirement plan as soon as you begin working. Even if you can only invest 2%, develop a habit of putting money (direct deposit) into a 401(k) or IRA.

4. Diversify your portfolio. Spread your investments among large, medium, small and foreign companies.

5. Take advantage of tax benefits, such as education-funding plans and home ownership.

Spending

1. Are you a spender, saver or somewhere in-between? Know your money personality and strive for balance.

2. Carry cash whenever possible. Psychologically, it is harder to spend cash than to use a credit card. This way you can eliminate credit card debt and borrow sparingly.

Family & Finances

1. Protect yourself and your family by having adequate insurance. Check your coverage for health, life, disability and home.

2. Begin a college savings account when your children are born. Establish a 529 plan early in a child's life, and you will allow time and compounding interest to work toward your child's college future. But remember… Fund your retirement account before you fund your child's college fund. You can get a loan to go to college, but there is no loan available for retirement.

3. Pay it forward. Give a share of stock or open an investment account as an added birthday or graduation gift.

4. Begin discussing money with children as soon as they express interest in an honest and age-appropriate manner.

5. Talk to your parents and know where their emergency information is located. Ask what plans they have made and how you can be of help.

Slow Cooker Turkey Chili

Send your ghosts and goblins (or Darth Vaders and Pokémons) out to Trick-or-Treat with a hearty supper like this Turkey Chili.

INGREDIENTS

1 Tbsp.	olive oil
1 cup	onion, chopped
1/2 cup	red bell pepper, chopped
1 Tbsp.	fresh garlic, minced
1 lb.	lean ground turkey breast
1 1/2 tsp.	sea salt
1/2 tsp.	red chili flakes
1/4 tsp.	black pepper
15 oz.	canned red kidney beans, drained and rinsed
15 oz.	canned black beans, drained and rinsed
15 oz. can	Muir Glen organic tomato sauce
15 oz.	low-sodium chicken stock
1 Tbsp.	chili powder
2 tsp.	cumin
1 tsp.	dried oregano

PREPARATION

- Heat oil in a large sauté pan. Add onion, red bell pepper and garlic. Sauté until onions are translucent.
- Add the ground turkey breast, salt, chili flakes and black pepper. Brown over medium heat until the turkey is cooked through.
- Pour the mixture into a crock pot.
- Add remaining ingredients and stir well to combine. Cook for 8 hours on low or 3-4 hours on high, stirring occasionally.

NUTRITIONAL ANALYSIS
Makes 10 (1 cup) servings. Each serving contains approximately:

200	calories
21 g.	protein
24 g.	carbohydrates
2 g.	fat
39 mg.	cholesterol
472 mg.	sodium
8 g.	fiber

Strong families make strong women

Dear Mom,

Yankee Doodle Dandy

My happy day

I write this note to thank you for everything that you have done for our family, and especially for all of your children. Thanks for the love, care and fun times that are embedded in our memories forever. The lessons of life that were taught while you were being the budget balancer, the taxi-cab driver, a dietician, a domestic engineer, a teacher, a spiritual counselor and a GREAT Mother will always be remembered.

Lessons of Life... You gave me a great leadership role model by being the best home-room Mom in school – you. You taught me that if you were going to do something, to do it right, by helping rip out the seams numerous times of my 4-H project. You instilled in me the importance to dream and imagine, by lying with me on the grass and picking out "monsters, angels and hearts" in the fluffy clouds on beautiful summer afternoons. You drove the competitive spirit in me, as you assisted me in dressing up and consistently winning the "Tacky Parade" contest.

More Lessons of Life... You demonstrated to me how to courageously handle death and disappointment, as you participated in our "cat funerals" complete with songs, a cross and prayer. You taught me that persistence was more important than being the most talented, as you pushed me down the hill on my red bike thousands of times so that I could learn to ride. You showed me how to love, as you took care of the elderly lady in the neighborhood when she had no air conditioning – yet you allowed her to lay in our house, on your bed, and with my Mommy.

Most Important Lessons of Life... You taught me the importance of my spiritual health, by ensuring that I was in church, was told Bible stories, and, most importantly, knew who my Savior was. You taught me to have FUN in life, by showing me how to cruise Sonic, while you ducked so that my friends would not know that you were in the car.

For everything – especially the GREAT lessons of life, THANK YOU!!!! I only hope and pray that I can be half the teacher, mentor, counselor, memory maker to my children that you have been to me!!!

I LOVE YOU!!!!

Debbie

MEDICATION SAFETY

As children, we always knew we could run to Mom...

...when we scraped our knees, had a tummy ache or a sore throat. We had the confidence that Mom would know just what to give us to "make it all better." Be sure you continue that tradition by following the valuable information in this chapter.

Your Medications

1　Develop a relationship with your pharmacist – he or she can answer many questions about your current and new medications. Try to use the same pharmacy for all of your prescription needs – this will help develop familiarity.

2　Before you leave the pharmacy, read the label of your prescription to make sure you understand dosage requirements, how to take the medication (with/without food), potential side effects, etc. Also, be sure to check that the label matches the information you discussed with your doctor.

3　Pharmacists are also a great resource for over-the-counter medication information. They can guide you to make the right decision to determine which over-the-counter medications can best suit your needs.

4　If you are currently taking medication, check with a health care professional before taking new medications to make sure they are compatible. Never give medicines to anyone other than for whom they were prescribed.

5　Keep a medication record up-to-date and show it to your doctor at each appointment. It should include all prescription, over-the-counter and herbal products you are taking, as well as your history of taking these medications.

6　Search the Internet for information about the medications you are taking. Most companies have Web sites with information about their products.

7 Read brochures and health information that are provided at your doctor's office and don't be afraid to ask questions about the articles and information.

8 Read the patient information materials provided with your prescriptions. Talk to your pharmacist and be sure to ask questions, particularly when using a new medication or if you have a new change in dosage.

9 Record and report all side effects of your medication to your doctor. This information is not only helpful to you and your treatment plan – it can be shared with the Food & Drug Administration (FDA) to update safety information in product labeling.

Your Medicine Cabinet

1 Inventory your medicine cabinet and first-aid kits at least once a year. Replace any missing materials and throw away expired prescription medications, as well as over-the-counter remedies.

2 Overdosing on medications and vitamins create a very serious health risk. Make sure you read the dosage guidelines carefully on any medication you are taking.

3 If medications are not in their original containers or are labeled unclearly, throw them away.

4 Keep the medicine cabinet locked for children's safety.

5 Always make sure that your medicine cabinet is well-stocked for everything from emergencies to medications for the common cold. For a list of what you should keep in your medicine cabinet, log on to www.speakingofwomenshealth.com.

Be sure you know what to do in case of poisoning. Keep both syrup of ipecac and activated charcoal on hand, but only administer after speaking to the poison control center or 9-1-1. The Poison Control Hotline is 1-800-222-1222.

Potato Salad

When you plan and fill your family's picnic basket, surround Mom's Old Fashioned Potato Salad with whole wheat bread and fresh fruit (both have fiber), and thoughtful beverages. And be sure to clean those hands before you eat!

INGREDIENTS

2 lbs.	potatoes
1 tsp.	salt
1 tsp.	black pepper
2	hard-boiled eggs
1 cup	celery, diced
1/2 cup	red onion, chopped
1/2 cup	red bell pepper, chopped
2 Tbsp.	Dijon mustard
1/2 cup	low-fat sour cream
2 Tbsp.	canola mayonnaise
1 tsp.	sugar
2 Tbsp.	vinegar

Cook's Note:
Although any potato works for this recipe, red skin or creamer potatoes have a very nice texture and do not require peeling.

PREPARATION

- Place potatoes in large saucepan with enough water to steam. Cover and steam about 1 hour until tender. Drain and cool.
- Dice potatoes and season with salt and pepper.
- In a small bowl mash hard boiled eggs.
- Combine celery, red onion and red bell pepper into small bowl with mashed eggs.
- In a large bowl, combine Dijon mustard, sour cream, canola mayonnaise, sugar and vinegar. Mix well.
- Add vegetable mixture to dressing and mix well.
- Add potatoes to dressing and vegetables and mix well.

NUTRITIONAL ANALYSIS
Makes 6 (1/2 cup) servings. Each serving contains approximately:

220	calories
6 g.	protein
31 g.	carbohydrates
8 g.	fat
80 mg.	cholesterol
515 mg.	sodium
4 g.	fiber

The graduation of a strong woman

Beverly and her Mom

Dear Mom,

Childhood memories

This letter is long overdue and something that I hope will not come as a surprise to you. Over the years, there has been no one who has been there for me, and encouraged me, as consistently as you have. I am blessed to have you as my Mom.

When Daddy died, you took on the Herculean task of raising six kids and made it look easy. You had just lost the love of your life and knew that despite your own personal pain that you had to put your children first and keep living so that each of us could do the same. You took the time to teach us fundamental values and life-lessons that were critical for us to make our way in the world. When we shared special times, like holidays, you always took the time to make them memorable and to remind us about the importance of family.

Some of my fondest memories include music and the joy that music has brought to me, through you. Big band, Sinatra and arias were the backdrop for otherwise normal routines like chores and setting up new homes. Memories that now flood my mind when I hear even a note or two.

As time went by and your babies became free-thinking individuals with purpose, you became our biggest fan – directly to us and to anyone who would listen. I never doubted I would see your face in a crowd at graduations, games, performances and academic events. You were front and center.

Now we are raising our own children and facing choices and challenges both personally and professionally. There is not a day that passes without your influence and your legacy reminding me of the right path. I ask myself, "What would Mom do?" and pass these lessons on to my Elizabeth in an effort to encourage her good-judgment and to keep her grounded, the way that you did for me.

Thank you for your unfailing quick wit – even through adversity – and thank you for your amazing integrity, grace and poise. And thank you, most of all, for teaching me to be the very best Mother and woman that I could possibly be. Just like you.

All of my love and admiration,

Bevly

HEADACHES

All Moms have headaches –

most are relieved by the time their children pass their teenage years. Seriously, talk with your family members about your family's history, because some types of headaches, like migraines, are thought to be inherited. The most common headaches are stress-related. Read these tips and talk to your pharmacist or health care provider about options for relief from symptoms.

Nearly half of the people in the United States who suffer from headaches do not seek treatment, and usually go undiagnosed and untreated. That's unfortunate because there is much you can do to get relief. Today, doctors are armed with new types of prescription medications that treat headaches, especially migraines, in different ways… bringing relief to millions.

Migraines

Migraines come in two types. **Common migraines** are usually on one side of the head, have a throbbing, intense pain near the eye of the affected side and are often associated with sensitivity to noise and light. **Classic migraines** may produce an "aura," or warning sign before their onset. Visual symptoms, like flashing lights, spots or zigzag lines that can appear in the eyes are also common. This aura can last for 10 – 40 minutes, and after the aura ends is usually when headache pain starts.

Symptoms of a migraine can include a sharp, throbbing pain on one side of the head, nausea, vomiting and sensitivity to noise and light.

Types of Headaches

There are several headache types:

1. Tension headaches, caused by stress or anxiety.

2. Cluster headaches, which occur again and again over time and have a shooting pain.

3. Hormonal headaches, which are caused by changes in your body's hormones. More than 60% of women can trace the root of their headaches to their menstrual cycle.

4. Sinus headaches are usually associated with constant pain and tenderness in the facial area and are accompanied by other symptoms of sinus disease such as nasal discharge, ear sensations or fullness, and facial swelling.

5. Migraines are vascular headaches – where the brain's blood vessels constrict due to certain triggers, and then dilate due to lack of oxygen. This constriction and dilation produces a pain cycle.

Preventing & Minimizing Headaches

1. Maintain a healthy lifestyle, including adequate sleep and proper diet and exercise to prevent or reduce headaches. Be sure you drink plenty of water to maintain proper hydration. Dehydration is a common cause of headaches.

2. Identify triggers for your headaches and migraines such as specific foods, stress, etc. Triggers can also include bright lights, certain foods, change in sleep patterns or sleep deprivation, fatigue, dehydration, menstruation or fluctuations in weather.

3. Keep a headache diary if you have frequent headaches. It can help to identify headache types, triggers and effectiveness of medicines.

4. Headaches can be symptoms of an impending cold, flu, sinus infection or other common illness. Your pharmacist can help with recommendations to bring relief.

5. Two goals for controlling any headache are relieving the current pain and preventing future attacks. Many headache sufferers use relaxation techniques and other exercises to relieve pain, and use these techniques to prevent further pain.

Seek medical attention if your headache is accompanied by severe head pain, vomiting, any neurological symptom (speech disturbances, vision blurring), any numbness or weakness in your body, or any problems concentrating or remembering information.

Treatment

1. Treatment for headaches and migraines can include over-the-counter or prescription medications, in combination with complementary therapies or alternative lifestyle approaches, such as Yoga, breathing exercises, acupuncture and biofeedback.

2. Consider discussing available treatment plans with your health care provider or pharmacist. A strong partnership is the first step in creating an effective plan to prevent and manage headaches and migraines.

3. If you are taking preventive medicines, be sure to follow dosage recommendations on the label. Take medications early – they can work better if taken earlier in a headache.

4. Be careful of mixing medications – even herbal medicines can have drug interactions.

5. If the nature of your headaches or migraines changes, inform your doctor. There may be a new cause that requires treatment.

6. To ease the discomfort and tension of a headache, try taking a warm bath, putting a hot or cold pack on your head or neck, going outside for some fresh air or taking a short nap.

French Vanilla Cheesecake

Since your birthday only comes once a year, indulge yourself and feed your soul with this amazing Cheesecake.

INGREDIENTS

1 cup	graham cracker crumbs
2 Tbsp.	unsweetened applesauce
2 cups	non-fat cottage cheese
2 cups	light cream cheese
1/2 cup	yogurt cheese
3	eggs
1 Tbsp.	all-purpose flour
3/4 cup	sugar
1	vanilla bean
1 Tbsp.	vanilla extract
1 cup	unsweetened frozen cherries
1/4 cup	sugar

Cook's Note:

Yogurt cheese can be made by wrapping yogurt in cheesecloth and inverting over an open container. Place in refrigerator overnight and excess water in the yogurt will drip to the bottom of the container. The remaining yogurt cheese will be richer and creamier. Cherries were inadvertently omitted from photo.

NUTRITIONAL ANALYSIS
Makes 16 servings. Each serving contains approximately:

175	calories
9 g.	protein
20 g.	carbohydrates
6 g.	fat
59 mg.	cholesterol
328 mg.	sodium
	trace fiber

PREPARATION

- Preheat oven to 325 degrees. Lightly coat a 10-inch spring form pan with canola oil.

- In a medium bowl, combine graham cracker crumbs and applesauce. Mix well. Press into the bottom of spring form pan. Set aside.

- Bring 1 cup of water to a boil in a small saucepan. Add vanilla bean and simmer until softened, about 1 minute. Remove from water and when cool enough to handle, slit bean lengthwise. Scrape out vanilla bean paste with a knife and reserve.

- In a blender container, puree cottage cheese until smooth. In a mixing bowl, combine pureed cottage cheese, cream cheese and yogurt cheese and blend with electric mixer on high until smooth, about 2 minutes. Add eggs, one at a time and blend well. Add flour, sugar, vanilla bean paste and vanilla extract. Blend well. Pour into crust.

- Bake for 40 minutes. Turn off heat to oven and allow cheesecake to cool slowly in oven for 30 minutes more. Remove from oven and let rest for 20 minutes before refrigerating.

- In a medium saucepan, combine cherries with sugar and bring to a boil. Reduce heat and simmer until sugar is dissolved and cherries begin to break down, about 10 minutes. Add water, if necessary, to keep from scorching.

- When cheesecake is cold, remove spring form sides and slice into 16 portions. Serve 1 Tbsp. cherries over cheesecake.

Mami,

*A sketch I made of
me wanting to be
"just like Mom"...*

...and you can see why!

You asked me so innocently why I spoil you so much? It is me, simply doing for you, as you taught me – by example. You gave me the greatest gift of all. You showed me what it is to be selfless.

You give without expectations. You guide me to be more. You inspire me to dream big. You nourish to make me stronger. You laugh when I smile. You show me hope. You empower me with the value of hard work. You show me how to appreciate everything and everyone. You demonstrate how to embrace my health and life. You teach me how to give and give in. You educate me on how to keep my promises with integrity and compassion. You've held me when I cried – and knew when not to ask why I cried. Even though it can be scary for a Mom, you encouraged me to think freely. You disciplined to make me grow. You exhibit affection, faith and love. With your actions I have seen what it is to trust, be trusted and to trust life.

I indulge in the joy of your company as your child, an adult, my friend and now Grandmother to my son.

As a new Mom I have learned my most precious commodity is time... something you have never denied me – your precious time.

I have faith in so many things because I can selflessly give and receive. I learned from you Mom – by example. Gracias.

With all my love,

Chef LaLa

HEALTHY EATING

Establish a daily diet low in fat,

high in fiber, rich in colorful fruits and vegetables, incorporating fish rich in Omega-3 fatty acids and plenty of water... but, also allow yourself the occasional indulgence of Mom's comfort foods and memorable desserts. Pampering yourself with small indulgences is food for the soul... just as good nutrition is fuel for your body.

Meal Time

1. Jump-start your mornings with a great breakfast to get you going. Each morning, we need to fuel our bodies so they work properly. Yet, many of us don't allow enough time to enjoy a proper breakfast.

2. Avoid skipping meals. Skipping meals may lower your metabolism and cause you to overeat at other times.

3. When faced with a tempting dessert, fried food or other treats, HALVE it and you can HAVE it! This simple trick works anytime, anywhere and can help you shed pounds while still eating the things you love!

4. Watch serving sizes... super-sizing doesn't mean super nutrition. A serving of meat is comparable to a deck of cards and can be held in the palm of your hand. When eating out and faced with an oversized portion, take a box home and save it for the next day's lunch or dinner.

5. Trade up for whole grains! The higher fiber, vitamin and mineral content of whole-grain breads, pastas and cereals will help you feel full on half the portion size. Eating more whole grains will also help you ward off diabetes and heart disease.

6. Choose either bread or dessert, not both.

7. In order to maintain a balanced diet, foods should include equal balances of grains, vegetables, fruits, milk, meat and beans. Most experts agree that the average woman requires about 2,000 calories each day.

8   Remember to balance your plate with variety. To maintain a healthy diet, each of us needs protein, carbohydrates and healthy fats. For more information about the amounts that you should be getting every day, visit our healthy nutrition page at www.speakingofwomenshealth.com.

9   One way to reduce blood pressure is to check nutrition labels for sodium content in the foods you eat. If you feel the need to add a little seasoning to your food, try herbs and spices or other seasonings to give it a natural flavor without the sodium.

Snacks

1   Do not allow long periods of time between eating. Try to consume three or more healthy meals plus healthy snacks in between.

2   Make your healthy foods available, visible and easy to eat. Leave the bananas out on your counter so you can grab one on-the-go in the morning. Cut up fruits and vegetables and put them in plastic bags for easy snacking.

3   Keep a variety of healthy packaged snacks on hand for a quick treat or pick-me-up. Choose multi-grain snack bars and portion-controlled packages of cookies and crackers. These convenient snacks can be a great way to satisfy a hunger.

Nutrition & Family

1   To keep your children interested in good nutrition, try some tips to make eating fun and nutritious. Use cookie cutters for sandwich art. Instead of bread, try using pita, whole grain crackers or soft tortillas for sandwiches. Consider a meal replacement bar or protein bar as a mid-afternoon snack.

2   Having regular family meals is important! Not only are you more likely to serve delicious, nutritious meals for your family, but it also provides essential "family time" that everyone needs.

3   On school nights, involve your kids while packing their healthy lunches. Have them make a list of the healthy things they like and make sure they look for those together while you are grocery shopping. For safety's sake, make sure you clean out their lunchboxes with soap and water to keep bacteria from growing.

Enchiladas Raquel

I named this recipe in my book after my Mom, Raquel. She is such a good cook. The greatest memories growing up were often shared at the dinner table.

INGREDIENTS

1 lb.	ground beef, extra lean
12 oz.	potato, peeled and quartered
3 oz.	water
6 oz.	tomatoes, canned
1 tsp.	salt
2 cloves	garlic, peeled
4 oz.	onion, peeled and quartered
2	serrano chilies
4 cups	beef or vegetable stock
1 each	tostada (fried tortilla)
1/4 tsp.	pepper
1 dash	cumin
14	corn tortillas
12 oz.	crumbled cotija

NUTRITIONAL ANALYSIS
Makes 14 enchiladas. Sauce makes 4 1/2 cups. Each serving contains approximately:

180	calories
9 g.	protein
19 g.	carbohydrates
8 g.	fat
3 g.	saturated fat
5 g.	unsaturated fat
30 mg.	cholesterol
279 mg.	sodium
2 g.	fiber

PREPARATION

- Place meat, potatoes, ground beef and water in pot.
- Cover, cook over low-medium heat for 20 minutes, until potatoes are tender.
- Drain the juice and reserve.
- Mash the meat and potatoes together with a potato masher. Mix in 1/2 tsp. of salt.
- In a blender, add reserved juice, canned tomatoes, 1/2 tsp. of salt, garlic cloves, onions, serrano chiles, stock, tostada (to thicken sauce), pepper and cumin.
- Puree and transfer sauce into a saucepan.
- Simmer on low for 20 minutes.
- Dip tortilla into saucepan, carefully and quickly transfer onto a baking pan.
- Spoon 2 oz. of meat/potato filling onto the tortilla in an elongated manner.
- Roll the tortilla with the seam ending up at the bottom.
- Arrange rolls closely to one another.
- Repeat with each tortilla. Cover with more sauce.
- Place in an oven for 5-7 minutes at 375 degrees.
- Serve immediately.
- Sprinkle with crumbled cotija or queso fresco.

This is not a Canyon Ranch makeover recipe.

Dear Mom,

Three generations of Dove Chocolate lovers!

Sometimes it's startling how fast our life goes by and even more shocking when we blink and the entire world has changed. Contrary to your final words, it was me who was so lucky to have you as my Mom and the lessons you taught me will forever change my life. The Mom I am is a reflection of your best qualities – tender nurturer, careful planner, expert cake maker, short order cook, house doctor, patient homework critic and spirited cheerleader. Your lessons taught me so well.

It started early. I remember running home from school and you were always there anxious to hear the news of the day. No matter whether it was a grade school crisis or a major pitfall, you always knew how to calm my fears and get me back on track. Always eager and through every lens I looked, you had the loudest cheer, my biggest supporter. With spunk and spirit, I was your purpose and you enthusiastically outperformed. Even when my many years of schooling ended, your role of supporter didn't. Through job applications, rejection letters and career promotions, you remained the strongest cheerleader of my life.

You also let me explore and always allowed me to spread my wings just far enough. As much as my newfound independence tore at your nerves, you never dashed my dreams. Surely, you bit your tongue or held back the words just to allow me the freedom to learn life's lessons. When those lessons crushed my dreams, it was you who helped pick up the pieces and inspired me to keep my chin up and continue along the road, no matter how rocky. You were always there to bring the dreams back into my vision.

Amazing to know now what you were capable of even when you had your own dark days to face. When death was stealing you away from us prematurely, you were the family rock. I remember you would profess "I have had a life with no regrets, a grand and glorious life, don't cry for me for I am the lucky one." What an inspiration to life you were and forever will be.

It was me who was the lucky one to have you as my Mom...
Your Margarita

SIMPLE PLEASURES

The simplest of pleasures began with the loving touch from our Moms.

Then, the wonderful cookies that we baked together, and the trips to the store to choose that "special treat." As we get older, we do those same things for people that we love. And, let's not forget to enjoy simple pleasures for ourselves.

Benefits

1 Celebrate yourself. Although much of your time may revolve around others, it's critical that you maintain the things that you feel passionate about in your life.

2 If you love being outdoors, make sure you take the time to plan trips to go canoeing, hiking, biking on weekends in the mountains or on a family vacation. Make plans in advance for a great time and relaxing getaway.

3 Spur-of-the-moment plans can be fun, too! Subscribe to weekly e-mails advertising last-minute specials to great places you've never been. One day, you just might pack a bag and head out for a wonderful getaway planned in 5 minutes!

4 If you're passionate about "date night" with your spouse or partner, don't give up that dinner and a movie or a concert. You will feel fresh and vital after an evening away from the daily stresses. If an evening away is too complicated, arrange a lunch or take in a matinee.

5 Being your best also means looking and feeling your best. Take a little time for an "at home" spa day. Color your hair, take a long bath and give yourself a manicure. Turn off the TV and turn on some soothing music. Light some candles and relax with your favorite book in your most comfortable clothes.

6 Don't let friends drift away – even if you think you are "too busy." A 30-minute walk, talking and laughing with a friend, is more than just exercise. It refreshes your vitality and rejuvenates your relationships.

7 As women, we often hesitate to say exactly what we need or give specific direction. Our friends and loved ones aren't mind readers. It's important to be explicit – if you want a day off from the everyday routine, the simple phrase "I'm tired" doesn't communicate that. Say what you mean and what you expect. Loved ones will be happy to contribute to your simple pleasures.

8 Know that everyday gifts always surround us… from the joy of waking up every morning to the small ways our loved ones show they care.

9 "You have to be present to win" is true for door prizes… and for life. Make sure you take an active role in your life – don't just LET things happen to you. You're worth it… take control!

10 Most of what we worry about on a regular basis never happens or isn't as big of a deal as we make it out to be. Concentrate on the things you can control and make positive changes.

11 If you train your eyes, you can change your life. If you begin looking for the good in every situation and every person you'll inevitably find it.

12 Open your mind to receiving lessons from unlikely teachers. Lessons are not always overt – be aware that you might be learning, even when you don't realize it!

13 Recognize your needs and differentiate between "needs" and "wants." Find healthy ways to meet your needs to boost self-esteem and cultivate a happy, balanced life.

14 It's great to indulge in a treat of tasty dark chocolates or a savory red wine occasionally. The key is moderation!

Sylvia's Chicken Scallopine

Dean Martin would have sang a different tune to "That's Amore" had he tried Sylvia's Chicken Scallopine first! Make this meal for your guests, and they'll know you've prepared it with love.

INGREDIENTS

4	skinned chicken breast halves, boned and defatted
½ cup	all-purpose flour
2 Tbsp.	Parmesan cheese, grated
3 tsp.	olive oil
2 tsp.	butter
1 Tbsp.	minced garlic
⅓ cup	white wine
1 Tbsp.	capers
1 tsp.	lemon peel
2 Tbsp.	lemon juice
¼ cup	chicken stock
¼ tsp.	salt
pinch	ground black pepper
2 cups	angel hair pasta, cooked
2 Tbsp.	parsley, freshly chopped

PREPARATION

- With a meat mallet, pound chicken breasts to ½-inch thick. In a small bowl, combine flour and cheese. Dredge both sides of chicken breast in flour mixture.

- In a large sauté pan, sauté chicken breasts in 1 tsp. olive oil for 3 to 5 minutes on each side or until cooked through. Remove from pan.

- Heat butter and remaining olive oil together over medium-low heat. Add garlic and cook 1 minute. Add wine and simmer for about 3 minutes or until wine is evaporated. Add remaining ingredients except salt, pepper and parsley. Simmer sauce for 5 more minutes. Add salt and pepper.

- Serve each chicken breast with 2 Tbsp. sauce and ½ cup cooked angel hair pasta and parsley.

NUTRITIONAL ANALYSIS
Makes 4 servings. Each serving contains approximately:

390	calories
33 g.	protein
35 g.	carbohydrates
10 g.	fat
80 mg.	cholesterol
301 mg.	sodium
2 g.	fiber

Dear Mom,

The Songbird
of the South

Speaking of Women's Health's
Queen of Gospel and her Mom

I was thinking about you and what a blessing you've been in my life, and several unforgettable moments came into my mind.

I can remember going to Birmingham, Alabama every summer listening to my "Big Mama" Solony Golds singing around the house and in the church choir. That's when singing was birthed into my spirit through my Great Grandmother "Big Mama." Being the oldest of 10 children, I realized Daddy was not financially prepared for me to take part in all the musical activities in school. But God always has a ram in the bush. However, I appreciate your unselfish spirit of allowing Mrs. Arlene Kirk and Mary G. Sanders to become my "Godmothers." Their invaluable contributions assisted me in reaching my dream of becoming successful in the music industry today.

And, yes, I can remember your unusual psychology when I did wrong. You made me get my own means of punishment, which was to pick several switches from a tree (smile). This punishment appeared to be harsh but it made me the woman I am today, teaching me discipline, to tell the truth, respect for others, and it developed within me a high level of integrity.

Mama, I have dined at some the finest restaurants in this country, but no chef can compare to your culinary skills; your cooking is blessed: Your Anointed BBQ ribs, your slap-somebody-dressing, your righteous sweet potato pie and your famous sugar cookies.

When the cupboard was nearly bare, you could take a little and turn into a lot that was sufficient to nourish our bodies. You have been a great influence in making me the cook that I am.

And, finally, I can remember a Christmas that is distinguished among all others. We did not have a traditional Christmas tree; however, the sofa served the same purpose. Still praying for a doll, I woke up and found not one, but several dolls, lined across the sofa. A caring and special person sent the dolls along with other goodies. Oh, what a Christmas my sisters Juanita, Tillie, Valarie and I had! It's one I will always cherish.

Well, I must close now, but always know that I am continually praying for your spiritual strength, good health and happiness.

Love Always,
Your Daughter

Dottie

HOLISTIC HEALTH

Just as "It takes a village to raise a child"...

...it also takes a village to keep yourself healthy... mind, body and spirit. Combining the wisdom of ages from our foremothers, with the research, technology and knowledge from our health care providers and pharmacists, allows us to create the village it takes to have a long, healthy and happy life.

As with any new program that impacts your health, you should talk with your health care provider before you begin an alternative medicine/complementary therapy regimen. Both you and your physician benefit from sharing information on herbal supplement usage and alternative therapies. Periodically reassess the need to continue this type of therapy, based on your progress.

Approaches

1 Integrative medicine involves using many therapies together, whether they are alternative or more conventional. For example, chemotherapy patients may combine prescription medication, ginger tea for nausea and meditation for relaxation to help relieve any side effects.

2 Holistic medicine, which encompasses acupuncture, herbs, massage and light exercise (such as Tai chi) can treat not only symptoms, but the root of the problem that causes the symptoms.

3 Ayurveda or ayurvedic medicine deals with the measures of healthy living, along with therapies that relate to physical, mental, social and spiritual harmony. It can be used to create balance in many kinds of relationships.

To create ayurvedic balance in relationships, elements of nature are usually used. For example, eating foods in a state as close to nature as possible is an element of ayurvedic medicine. To ease irritability, take a friend out into nature for a day of leisure and eat mild, cooling foods.

4 Acupuncture is the insertion of fine needles into specific acupuncture points along the energy meridians to help release blocks and restore energy flow. Blood circulation is enhanced and better able to nourish tissues and begin the healing process.

Research has shown that acupuncture may boost the body's immune response and has been used as a form of adjunct therapy for many illnesses.

5 The Alexander Technique is a method that works to change movement habits in our everyday activities. It is a simple and practical method for improving ease and freedom of movement, balance, support and coordination.

6 Feng shui is an ancient Chinese practice of placement and arrangement of space to achieve harmony with the environment. Feng shui addresses specific areas of the body, because each area is related to different areas of your home, with the center of your home related to overall balance. This includes overall health... when you are out of balance, ill health can result.

Many practitioners believe that good feng shui in the bedroom is essential for optimal rest and good health. The bed should face the door, but should not be in a direct line with the bedroom door or bathroom door. Keep the bathroom door shut. Add greens, blues and neutral colors in the bedroom. Remove all work, laundry, stacks of magazines, books and projects from your bedroom... it should be a place of rest and relaxation.

7 Hospitals and medical clinics across the country are starting to integrate massage into patient care to help patients cope with stress and pain and as a therapeutic service for cancer patients and women who are pregnant.

The effects of reduced stress due to massage are well-documented. Massage has also been shown to reduce the formation of scar tissue after injury.

To remedy pain, add cheerful colors like yellow, upward-growing plants and happy pictures of yourself in your home. Remove drooping plants and sharp angles to increase your energy. Avoid pure white walls, as they invite stress into your home.

Herbs

1 When beginning an herbal supplement regimen, carefully read the labels of all products to make an informed decision. Talk with your pharmacist about potential side effects, allergic reactions and impact on the medication that you are currently taking.

2 Don't use herbal products during pregnancy unless your doctor recommends them. Some women use ginger for pregnancy-associated nausea upon the advice of their physicians; however, most herbs have not been studied in pregnant women or in women who are trying to become pregnant.

3 Plant an herb garden close to the kitchen. Get your children involved – when they become involved, they are much more adventurous and open to new foods.

4 There are more than 5,000 herbs within holistic pharmacopoeia. Herbs are combined together into formulas to bring the body back to balance.

Chicken Teriyaki "Wings"

These Chicken "Wings" are a healthy version of a traditional favorite. They will fly off the platter at your next family gathering!

INGREDIENTS

4	skinned chicken breast halves, boned and defatted
½ cup	low-sodium wheat-free tamari soy sauce
2 Tbsp.	rice vinegar
3 tsp.	chopped fresh garlic
3 tsp.	fresh ginger, minced
1½ cups	thawed apple juice concentrate
½ cup	finely chopped green onions

PREPARATION

- Combine all ingredients except green onions and chicken in blender container and process. Stir in the onions.
- Place chicken in glass baking dish and pour the marinade over chicken. Marinate for 10 minutes to 1 hour. Turn chicken occasionally to distribute marinade evenly.
- Preheat grill or broiler. Grill or broil 5 to 10 minutes on each side or until chicken is cooked through.

NUTRITIONAL ANALYSIS
Makes 4 servings. Each serving contains approximately:

200	calories
27 g.	protein
13 g.	carbohydrates
3 g.	fat
72 mg.	cholesterol
402 mg.	sodium
	trace fiber

A beautiful model

Modeling with Mom

My role model

When I was a little girl, I would often accompany you as you posed for fashion photographers or gracefully high heeled it down a couture runway. It was many years later that I finally understood what role modeling played in your life. You taught me that you can take your God-given assets (beauty, brains) and use them to make other possibilities a reality. Your appearance was not an end, but a means. Little did I know that you were saving every penny you earned to be able to go to law school.

I cannot thank you enough for the one-liner you shared with me one autumn afternoon when I was about 9 years old. After finishing my homework, I'd wandered into the dining room where you were buried under miles of piles of law books. I was baffled. Why were you doing what I do – memorizing textbooks and studying for tests? I thought you were a Mom with a mission statement to raise five kids. When you said you were in law school, I was truly perplexed. I didn't know Moms could be lawyers too. You smiled and said, "In life, you can do anything you want to do."

As young as I was, that statement resonated with me. I watched as you rose to the multitasking challenge of completing your studies, starting companies with Dad, while still taking care of yourself and still being a Mom. I was exhausted just watching you in action. With your words of wisdom imprinted in my youthful mind, I suddenly felt unlimited freedom to dream. My whole world opened up. I set out to live my life filled with hope, seeing endless possibilities for personal and professional achievement and fulfillment.

That phrase became my credo as I constantly found myself in the unique position of being either the first (woman physician inducted into Maryland Rotary) or one of the few women (chief medical correspondents on television) in my field. I felt empowered every time I said, "Yes, I'll try that." I also incorporated Helen Keller's powerful proclamation that "Life is either a daring adventure, or nothing at all."

Armed with a self assertive attitude, I have forged ahead with my life's journey, less afraid to make mistakes, and eagerly embracing each challenge. You did it, and now I'm doin' it. Sorry, got to run. So much to do, so many dreams to live.

Pamela

HEALTHY AGING

CHAPTER 7

Florence Henderson always says...

..."My age is none of my business." As America's favorite Mom knows, age is just a number. The way you care for yourself and your attitude impact your "Real Age" just as much as the year of your birth.

Your Mind

1. The first step to looking more radiant and feeling more vibrant is to know that you're the right age right now – and you will be every day of your life.

2. Everything you do is either rejuvenating or aging you. You are in control! You alone have a choice about how to spend your time or what to order from a menu. Think about whether your choices are making you younger or older.

3. Value yourself so that self-care becomes second nature. Always wear sunblock, remove your makeup at night, use a good moisturizer, brush and floss your teeth, see your doctor regularly and take any medication precisely as prescribed.

4. Having passion is key to staying young. Whether it's your job, your hobby or a cause you believe in, a vitality and passion for what you do is a passport to youthfulness.

5. Think "MEN"... the key for graceful aging: Meditation, Exercise and Natural foods.

6. Quiet time and relaxation are keys to staying young. In a recent study, people who practiced meditation for more than 5 years were an average of 12 years younger physiologically (your "Real Age" can be quite different from your chronological age). Get quiet time by writing in a journal or simply sitting and concentrating on your breathing.

7. As you age, healthy exercise isn't just limited to physical fitness – mental exercises are needed to keep your mind sharp and fit! Play brain games and keep learning!

8 To exercise your brain, try learning a new language, work crossword puzzles, play Scrabble or Bridge. Soduku puzzles are a fun new trend that help keep your brain young.

9 Unload bad memories and stress. Stress causes the buildup of cortisol, which is not good for memory.

10 Ongoing mental stimulation throughout your life is the key to healthy brain aging. It's never too late to make lifestyle changes that may help preserve memory function.

Your Body

1 Forget chronological age – it's your functional and biological age that matter! Physical activity is the most influential thing on biological age.

2 Begin a small strength-training program. Weight training prevents sarcopenia, which is the age-related or disuse-related loss of lean body mass (muscle).

3 A healthy diet is healthy for your mind, body and spirit. Especially focus on eating a diet rich in a variety of foods, limiting saturated fats, eating Omega-3 fats and getting plenty of fruits and vegetables.

4 Antioxidants in natural and supplemental forms are key to healthy aging and preserving memory. Foods, including citrus fruits, berries and tomatoes will help in preserving your memory.

5 Pay attention to your numbers. Know your blood pressure and cholesterol levels to increase the years in your life and the life in your years!

6 Although the physical aging of our bodies is unavoidable, people age at widely different rates. Genetics has a major influence on how you age, along with environmental factors and lifestyle.

7 As we age, many of us develop sleep problems. Make sure to follow a regular schedule, try not to nap too much during the day, be careful about what you eat and don't use alcohol or smoke cigarettes to make you sleep. For more information, see Chapter 20.

Oatmeal Raisin Cookies

While in grammar school, I would race home with my older brothers every afternoon, bursting into the kitchen and hoping my Mother had baked her oatmeal raisin cookies. I staked my claim on the biggest one I could find, knowing my brothers would easily inhale the rest of the batch. With a cookie and glass of milk in hand, I'd sit at the kitchen table recounting the day's events to anyone within earshot. After savoring every bite and feeling re-energized, I'd bolt out the door, joining my friends to jump rope, bike or kick the ball. Fueled with my rolled oats and raisins, you'd best be able to find me hanging upside down, dangling off a tree limb, a blissfully happy, freckle-faced tomboy. Years later, as a nutrition and fitness expert, I updated the original recipe to include healthier ingredients. Funny, as I've gotten older, I've learned there is life after reducing the sugar and butter!

INGREDIENTS

- 1/4 cup   butter
- 1/3 cup   low-fat cream cheese
- 1 cup   brown sugar
- 1   egg yolk
- 3/4 tsp.   pure vanilla extract
- 3/4 cup   all-purpose flour
- 1 1/2 cups   rolled oats
- 3/4 tsp.   baking powder
- 3/4 tsp.   cinnamon
- 1/2 tsp.   salt
- 1/2 cup   raisins

PREPARATION

- Preheat oven to 350 degrees.
- Lightly coat a baking sheet with canola oil.
- In a large bowl, combine butter, cream cheese and brown sugar. Add egg yolk and vanilla extract and mix briefly.
- Combine remaining ingredients in a large bowl. Add to creamed mixture and mix until all dry ingredients are moistened.
- Portion heaping teaspoonfuls of dough, about 3/4 oz. onto baking sheet about 1 1/2-inches apart. Bake for 7 minutes. Lightly flatten with finger. Rotate baking sheet and bake for 4 minutes.

NUTRITIONAL ANALYSIS
Makes 38 cookies. Each cookie contains approximately:

75	calories
1 g.	protein
13 g.	carbohydrates
2 g.	fat
15 mg.	cholesterol
49 mg.	sodium
1 g.	fiber

Dear Mom,

A woman of strength,
character and commitment

Mom - still cooking for us with
the finest ingredients
and a heart full of love

Hedy and her resilient Mom

You were never one to express feelings or emotion; rather, it's the focus you have always had on tangible, everyday activities and responsibilities that shaped me over the years.

As a 16 year-old girl in Poland at the beginning of World War II, you were summoned from your parents' home by German soldiers and assigned to work as a servant for a music publisher and his wife and child in Germany. You hadn't seen your parents for 6 years by the end of the war when you hired an underground repatriation service that stole your belongings but brought you to the displaced persons camp where your Mother and Father were located. You've told me that story several times along with the memory that when you were reunited after so many years apart, one of the first things Grandma did was scold you for having lost your clothes. I've never forgotten that. My heart aches for you still today as I think of the anticipation you must have had for a loving reunion and the practicality with which you were greeted.

Mom, I will always see you as a perpetually busy woman who measures a successful day by how many baskets of clothes were laundered and ironed; how many jars of tomatoes were canned; and especially, how well the evening's dinner was received and appreciated. In the end, it was always the food, prepared from scratch and with the best ingredients, that was your expression of love for Dad and us kids. And nothing ever pleased you more than the compliments you received for your efforts. I have come to respect both the experiences that shaped you and the simple commitments you made to your family, your faith and your home. As I encounter my own life challenges, I seek comfort in the knowledge that I come from tough stock; that the women in my lineage endured great hardships and thrived. And I remind my own Daughters of the strength of their heritage whenever I hear them doubt themselves.

I have never faced the fears of hunger or loneliness or survival that you endured at a young age. I know that in comparison to such actual danger the things that I sometimes worry about are trivial and unimportant. So, Mom, your gift to me has been confidence in my ability to endure and an appreciation for the basic priorities of life.

With much love and respect,

Hedy

HEALTHY PREGNANCY

Congratulations! Your Mom is about to become a Grandmother...

...and her little girl is about to be a Mom! Since this is a book dedicated to Mothers, we want to provide some resources you'll need to become a healthy Mother – and to deliver a healthy, vibrant baby.

Prenatal Suggestions

1. Be sure to seek prenatal care as soon as you think you're pregnant. It's important to both your baby and you. Some doctors recommend that women planning to become pregnant plan a visit to talk about pre-pregnancy health and nutrition tips.

2. Good nutrition is vital for everyone... but, especially expectant Moms. Each day, be sure to eat foods high in fiber (from whole grains), and low in fat; eat plenty of protein, fruits and vegetables and top it off with low-fat milk to ensure baby's strong bones.

3. If you experience nausea or morning sickness, consider eating 5 or 6 small meals a day instead of 3 large ones.

4. Drink extra fluids (water is preferred) throughout your pregnancy to help your body keep up with increases in blood volume. Drink between 6-8 glasses of water, fruit juice or milk each day.

5. Take 400 mg of folic acid daily both before pregnancy and during the first few months to reduce the risk of birth defects of the brain and spine. Taking vitamins every day during your pregnancy is also best to ensure your baby's health. Your health care provider should guide you.

6. Limit caffeine and avoid alcohol during pregnancy. There is no safe amount of alcohol a woman can drink while pregnant. Caffeine should also be limited. There are plenty of "better for you" options like caffeine-free sodas, juices, teas or flavored waters.

7. Physical activity during pregnancy can be beneficial for both your baby and you. Talk with your midwife or doctor about effective exercises that reduce the impact on your baby and help you stay fit. Good choices include Yoga, swimming and walking.

8   Know your limits. Let your physician know if you experience pain of any kind, strong cramps, uterine contractions, vaginal bleeding, leaking of amniotic fluid, dizziness, fainting, shortness of breath, palpitations, trouble walking, joint swelling or if your baby has decreased activity.

9   Be sure to get plenty of rest (enjoy it while you can!). Rest on your side as often as possible, especially on your left side, to promote circulation and reduce swelling.

10 It is generally recommended that a woman of normal weight before pregnancy gain between 25 and 35 pounds during pregnancy. Make sure you maintain a healthy diet to get your body into shape post-pregnancy.

Notes on Happy Babies

1   During the first set of check-ups, there are many things doctors look for to ensure that your baby is growing and healthy. Weight, length and head size are all measured and compared to an age-specific and gender-specific growth chart. Your doctor might ask you about basic milestones like smiling, rolling over and pulling up to make sure your child is on target with normal development. A physical exam is also conducted to make sure vessels are properly working, eyes and ears are seeing and hearing, the crown of the head is growing, and the spine and skin are properly growing. Sleeping routines, eating routines and regular vaccination schedules are also discussed.

2   Believe it or not, babies communicate by crying! Remember that crying is a baby's first language and the best way for your newborn to communicate with you.

3   If your newborn is crying, picking her up is OK! Some parents worry that picking up a baby every time she cries promotes too much attention. Studies actually show that babies who are tended to promptly will actually cry less often and for shorter periods of time by the end of the first year.

4   Some ways to stop your baby from crying include dancing, rocking, giving a gentle backrub, singing, getting some fresh air, going for a stroller ride or going for a short ride in the car.

Enjoy quiet moments rocking your baby and listening to music. Cherish these special moments; they are soothing to both your baby and you. According to research, listening to classical music, even before birth, helps to develop logic and critical thinking for life.

Grandma's Horns

Generations of family recipes are wonderful to share. You might consider making a "Family Favorite Recipe Book" for a holiday gift.

INGREDIENTS

Dough

1 1/4 cups	butter
3	egg yolks, beaten
1 pkg.	dry yeast
1 cup	sour cream
4 cups	flour
3/4 tsp.	salt
2 tsp.	vanilla

Horn Filling

7 oz. tube	almond paste
1/4 cup	sugar
14	Zwieback toasts, crushed
1 stick	butter
2	egg whites
1 tsp.	almond extract

Powder Sugar Frosting

1 Tbsp.	butter, melted
1 1/2 cups	powder sugar
3 tsp.	fresh orange juice
3 tsp.	fresh lemon juice
3 tsp.	dark rum

NUTRITIONAL ANALYSIS
Makes 48 servings. Each serving contains approximately:

180	calories
3 g.	protein
19 g.	carbohydrates
11 g.	fat
33 mg.	cholesterol
40 mg.	sodium
1 g.	fiber

PREPARATION

Dough

- Mix together flour, salt and yeast. Cut butter into flour. Add egg yolks, sour cream and vanilla. Kneed and form into ball. Flour board with powder sugar. Divide dough into 6 portions. Roll each portion in a 12-inch circle. Spread each with filling. Cut each circle into 8 wedges. Roll up wedges, starting at widest edge. Bake 15 minutes at 350 degrees until slightly brown. Frost with powder sugar frosting.

Horn Filling

- Beat butter. Add paste and sugar. Add egg whites and almond extract. Mix. Add Zwieback and mix.

Powder Sugar Frosting

- Melt butter in a sauce pan. While over a low heat, add half the sugar and lemon and orange juices. Mix well. Add remaining sugar, juices and rum. Keep stirring until the frosting is thick and glossy.

This is not a Canyon Ranch makeover recipe.

Visiting In Holden

Recent arrivals in Holden from Culver City, Calif., are MR. and MRS. ROBERT W. HAMILTON and their children (from left), SUSAN GERTRUDE, and the twins, ANNE WING and CAROL JOHNSON HAMILTON. They are guests of Mrs. Hamilton's parents, Mr. and Mrs. Henning L. Johnson of 13 Fairchild Drive, Holden.

In the news...read all about it

My Mom left us suddenly without enough warning last November.

I realized Mom made me love everything about being a girl. Girls could do anything – and should – without boundaries. She wanted me to have a career and to see the world. In grammar school we moved to Mexico City and she learned Spanish with us and encouraged us to learn how to do the Mexican Hat Dance! Then in high school we moved to England where we discovered European culture. She approached life as a wonderful adventure.

When we went to college, she began a career as a jewelry buyer, showing me you can have it all as a "girl."

She was beautiful with impeccable taste, and so she taught me beauty "from the inside out." Everyone loved my Mom. She was so much fun.

HEALTHY SKIN

The basics of good skincare have not changed for generations...

...cleanse, tone, moisturize and protect! The great news is... contemporary products give us a wonderful advantage in all four areas. Researchers now know what ingredients will help skin stay healthy, youthful and glowing. And, remember... the single most important thing you can do to improve your overall look is to SMILE!

Daily Care

Women usually begin to think about skincare in their teens and early 20s when acne pops up. As women enter their 30s, 40s, 50s and beyond, and the skin matures, concerns about fine lines and wrinkles spur them on to looking for a treatment product that keeps skin hydrated and provides skin protection.

1. There are four key steps to good skin health: Cleanse, Tone, Moisturize and Protect.

2. Your Mother was correct – remove your makeup before going to bed to promote better skin health. Cleanse your face to remove makeup, dirt and oil. This helps unclog pores and control acne breakouts.

3. A toner helps remove anything you missed while cleansing and also helps restore pH balance, reduces pore size and allows skin to accept your moisturizer.

4. Moisturize your skin every day to keep it supple and vitalized. Choose a moisturizer made specifically for your age and skin type. Many moisturizers include ingredients that help control acne, combat wrinkles and age lines, and lift and tone skin.

5. In a moisturizer, choose Vitamin A for increased cell turnover and anti-aging benefits, Vitamin C to reduce fine lines and wrinkles and Vitamin E for its skin-smoothing properties.

6. Make sun protection part of your daily skin routine... it's a great long-term investment. Choose a moisturizer with a Sun Protection Factor (SPF) of at least 15, and apply at least 30 minutes before heading out doors. Now, you can find lotions that are free of fragrance and enriched with vitamins. This helps keep your pores unclogged.

7. When out of doors, don't forget to reapply sunscreen every two hours, even on cloudy days. Why? Because UVA rays penetrate clouds, glass and even some plastics and are responsible for wrinkles and aging (think "A" for Aging). UVB rays cause a sunburn (think "B" for Burning). Both UVA and UVB rays may cause cancer.

8   If you can't live without a tan, why not try using a sunless tanning product? More than 90% of your skin's aging is due to excessive sun exposure. To achieve that natural healthy-looking glow, begin by exfoliating with a gentle scrub before applying a sunless tanner. To ensure even and natural coverage, use a sponge to blend the tanner on your face, paying close attention to your hairline, ears, chin and neck.

9   Don't forget about the rest of your body! Today's products go beyond soap and water to offer a nourishing experience that will leave your skin feeling fresh, smooth and hydrated.

10 The skin on your neck needs just as much care as the skin on your face. Make sure to cleanse, tone, moisturize and protect here, too.

11 Hydrate, hydrate, hydrate! Water is the most plentiful substance in the body. Drink water to establish a healthy diet and promote softer, more wrinkle-free and healthy skin.

12 There are a wide variety of products available for your skin's individual needs. Consider day and night creams, products formulated specially for eyes, lips, hands, feet and body and even different forms of products for different seasons.

Reminders

1   Once a week, use an exfoliation treatment to remove dead skin cells and stimulate cell turnover. Consider a scrub, glycolic peel or microdermabrasion to reduce fine lines and reveal healthier, younger-looking skin.

2   Check your skin often for signs of skin cancer. To get an idea of what skin cancer might look like, check out our Skin Health and Beauty page at www.speakingofwomenshealth.com.

3   Stop smoking! It's well-known that smoking is damaging to delicate skin, especially around the mouth and eyes.

4   Dry skin looks old. Avoid lots of long, hot baths and harsh soaps – both of which dry out your skin. Short showers with moisturizing soaps or body washes are best and should always be followed by applying a moisturizing lotion all over your body to keep your skin looking young.

5   If you're contemplating a cosmetic procedure, make sure you research the training and competence level of the person doing the procedure. There are many over-the-counter products available to reduce the effects of aging on your skin, but if you choose a cosmetic procedure, know the facts.

Chili Con Carne

Building snowmen (and women), ice skating and sledding can build up a hearty appetite. Try this delicious chili recipe to warm up even the coldest winter snow bunny.

INGREDIENTS

1 1/2 lbs.	ground beef, extra lean
1 Tbsp.	olive oil
1 cup	sweet onion, chopped
1 Tbsp.	garlic, minced
1/4 cup	yellow bell pepper, chopped
28 oz. can	crushed Muir Glen organic tomatoes, undrained
16 oz. can	red kidney beans, drained and rinsed
1 Tbsp.	chili powder
1 Tbsp.	sugar
2 cups	low-sodium chicken stock
1/2 tsp.	garlic powder
1 tsp.	Tabasco Sauce
1 1/2 tsp.	sea salt
1 tsp.	dried basil
1/2 tsp.	dried oregano

PREPARATION

- In a large saucepot, brown beef until cooked through, drain and set beef aside.
- In the same pot, add onions, bell pepper, garlic and olive oil and sauté over medium heat until onions are translucent.
- Add remaining ingredients and cooked beef. Stir well to combine. Reduce heat to low and simmer for 1 hour, stirring occasionally.

NUTRITIONAL ANALYSIS
Makes 6 (1 cup) servings. Each serving contains approximately:

370	calories
38 g.	protein
23 g.	carbohydrates
14 g.	fat
83 mg.	cholesterol
384 mg.	sodium
7 g.	fiber

"It takes a village" – *my women of influence*

Tribute to a Few GR-R-REAT Women

I have always adored my Mother, who was also my best friend, and provided me with unconditional love and support. Because of her, I chose my career path in nutrition (I thought understanding the relationship between diet and health would better enable me to counsel her on how to control hypertension).

I am also fortunate to have had several other "Mother figures" in my life. I refer to this group of women as my "posse." Although most of them, including my Mother, have passed on, I shall not forget their kind and nurturing support. In fact, they taught me that life is a journey, and not a destination, and that no matter what happens, each day is new and you get the chance to paint a different landscape. They passed along so many wise sayings that have become even more valuable and understandable as I have matured. These include such sayings as: "This too shall pass;" "Don't count your chickens before the eggs are hatched;" "Nothing spoils a duck but his bill;" "Put your trust in God and not in man;" "You don't miss your water until the well runs dry" and the list goes on and on.

How blessed I am to have had these GR-R-REAT women in my life who have helped mold and shape me into the woman I am today. I so very much appreciate them and the best way I can think to honor them is to pass it on – to my Daughter and young women like her – who stand ready to take the baton forward.

HEART HEALTH

The heart strings between Mothers and Daughters are woven with gold.

Our Moms healed our broken hearts when we were teens. Armed with all the knowledge we have about physically healthy hearts, today we can help heal our Moms' hearts and protect our own. Get started today and share this heart-felt information with the women you know and love.

Heart disease isn't just a man's disease... it's the number one cause of death in women. And, did you know the symptoms of a heart attack in women can be different than symptoms in men. They include a feeling of breathlessness, often without chest pain, flu-like symptoms, pain in the upper back, neck or jaw, feelings of anxiety, unexplained excessive fatigue or difficulty sleeping.

Risk Factors

1. Knowing your risk factors is key to staying heart healthy. Know your cholesterol, blood pressure, glucose, body mass index and personal and family history of heart disease.

2. Smoking and lack of exercise greatly increase your risk. Also, post-menopausal women are at a greater risk of developing heart disease.

3. Race is another factor in heart disease. African-American women are at greater risk of developing heart disease than Caucasian, Asian and Hispanic women.

4. Hypertension, or high blood pressure, is a very controllable risk factor. Because it is known as a silent killer, most people who have hypertension never feel sick.

5. Symptoms of peripheral vascular disease include dull pain in the leg after exercise, numbness or tingling in the leg or foot, ulcers or sores that do not heal properly or a noticeable change in skin color.

Prevention

1. Eating a heart-healthy diet will help guard against heart disease. Omega-3 fatty acids found in certain fish such as salmon and sardines are an excellent source of those all-important Omega-3 fatty acids. Oatmeal, red wine and wheat germ all include antioxidants, fiber and flavanoids that can protect against heart disease. There are many prepared foods that are now available that directly address eating to help prevent heart disease and stroke.

2. Trans-fats, or partially hydrogenated vegetable oils, raise the level of "bad" cholesterol in the blood. Look for snacks and margarines that say "no trans-fats."

3. Obesity has become an epidemic and is associated with many health problems, including high blood pressure, cancer, diabetes, arthritis and heart disease. Be sure to maintain a healthy weight for your body type.

4 Small changes can make a big difference in your heart health. Take the stairs instead of the elevator to increase your exercise. Cut fatty foods a little more each week to promote a healthy diet.

5 There are two types of cholesterol. HDL, or "healthy" cholesterol, protects us against heart disease. Exercise raises the level of HDL. LDL, or "lousy" cholesterol, comes from fatty foods and can lead to clogged arteries and heart disease. A desirable total cholesterol level is less than 200.

6 Before making changes to your lifestyle, know the status of your heart health. Get your cholesterol, blood pressure and blood sugar tested. Know your numbers for good heart health.

7 Treating post-menopausal women with HRT (hormone replacement therapy) does not protect them against developing atherosclerosis (hardening of the arteries). Talk to your health care provider to make the right decision for you about post-menopausal hormonal therapy and how to protect your heart as you age.

Stroke

1 Along with heart disease, women should know the warning signs of a stroke. These include sudden numbness or weakness of the face, arm or leg, especially on one side of the body; sudden confusion, trouble speaking or understanding; sudden trouble seeing in one or both eyes; sudden trouble walking, dizziness, loss of balance or coordination or sudden, severe headache with no known cause.

2 If given within the first three hours of symptoms, a clot-busting drug may reduce long-term disability for the most common type of stroke.

3 Because many of the risk factors, warning signs and prevention techniques are the same for heart disease, stroke and peripheral vascular disease, if you're protecting yourself from one, you're giving yourself a triple advantage!

4 Peripheral vascular disease is a vascular change usually found in the legs. It involves the buildup of plaque in the arteries and blocks the flow of blood to the leg from the heart. When vessels are blocked, muscles surrounding the artery do not receive the oxygen they need, causing pain in the hip or leg.

Be an Agent of Change...

Tell Your Mother

According to recent estimates, 1 in 3 adults has high blood pressure but don't know it due to lack of symptoms. Make sure to have your blood pressure checked regularly.

Collard Green Quiche

R oom temperature or right out the oven, this colorful quiche is perfect for an afternoon book club or gathering of friends. For appetizers, pour quiche in an 8 x 8-inch square pan and cut into small squares.

INGREDIENTS

Pie Crust

1 cup	all-purpose flour
1 tsp.	sugar
1/4 tsp.	salt
3 Tbsp.	butter
4 Tbsp.	cold water

Custard

2 slices	bacon, diced
1 1/2 cups	yellow onion, diced
8 oz.	collard greens, freshly chopped
1/2 tsp.	salt
1/4 tsp.	black pepper
4	whole eggs
2	egg whites
3/4 cup	fat-free milk
1/2 cup	half and half
1/2 cup	Swiss cheese, grated
1/2 tsp.	salt
1/4 tsp.	black pepper
pinch	nutmeg, freshly grated
1 Tbsp.	all-purpose flour

NUTRITIONAL ANALYSIS
Makes 8 servings. Each serving contains approximately:

225	calories
11 g.	protein
20 g.	carbohydrates
12 g.	fat
131 mg.	cholesterol
381 mg.	sodium
2 g.	fiber

PREPARATION

- Preheat oven to 350 degrees.

- In a small bowl, combine flour, sugar and salt. Mix well. Using a pastry cutter, blend in butter until mixture is crumbly and pea-sized. Add cold water, 1 Tbsp. at a time and gently mix after each addition. Mixture should begin to bind together after the last Tbsp. of water is added. If too dry, add 1 more Tbsp. of water. Gather mixture into a ball and let rest for 5 minutes.

- Lightly flour a flat surface and roll dough into a large circle, 12 to 14 inches in diameter. Gently press into a 9-inch pie pan and flute edges. Top dough with beans or pie weights and bake for 5-10 minutes or until crust is just beginning to turn golden brown.

- In a large sauté pan, cook the diced bacon until crispy. Add onions to pan and sauté until translucent.

- Add collard greens to the pan and season with salt and pepper. Cook for 1-2 minutes and drain any excess water from the pan. Allow to cool slightly.

- In a large bowl, combine eggs, egg whites, milk, and half and half. Whisk until well combined. Add cheese, salt, black pepper, nutmeg and sprinkle in flour. Stir in cooked collard greens.

- Pour into pre-baked pie shell and bake for 30-40 minutes or until filling is set. A knife inserted in the center will come out clean. Let cool slightly and cut into 8 slices.

Whether by horse...

...or by rail - Nonnie gets us there. My girls and I adore her!

A Woman of Influence

Being women, we can usually reflect on someone who has had an influence in our lives... Moms, friends, peers, aunts. For me it has been my Grandmother, or Nonnie, as I call her. She was in her early 40's when I arrived and she refused to be called "Grandma!"

Nonnie was widowed very young and raised 3 daughters on her own working as a Registered Nurse. Through her example, I learned that a woman can get an education, have a career and raise a family successfully. She was, and remains a strong, independent force in all of our lives.

I was just 4 years old when she put me on the back of a horse for the first time. She also dusted me off and made me get back on when I fell off that first time and every time thereafter. But it taught me that pursuing my passion of horses did not come easy or free. There was sometimes pain involved and a lot of responsibility.

By hitching up the RV every summer and taking us around the country, we grandkids fell in love with traveling and exploring. We would stop at KOA's across the United States, camping out and munching on her home made granola.

It was Nonnie who encouraged my childhood dream of attending the University of Arkansas, even arranging for a friend, who was housemother to a sorority, to give me a tour of the campus when I was still in high school. During college, she was there with food or a winter coat, knowing funds were tight as I worked myself through college. I remember once questioning how I would ever repay her for those times she was there. Her answer was to remember these moments because someone else would come along after me, and it would be my responsibility to be there for them.

Through her examples and guidance, she has demanded that I be strong and that I never back away from something just because it scares me. Throughout my life, she has shown me the type of woman and Mom that I want to be, and it is that example that I try to live so that my two Daughters can say that I was a strong influence in their lives.

Lee Anne

MOTHER EARTH

In a book dedicated to Moms, let us take a moment to honor the Mom we all share...

...Mother Earth. These thoughtful "notes" will help sustain the environment around us and preserve our natural ecosystems for future generations. And, let us not forget, personal sustainability. In order to maintain your natural balance, pamper yourself by creating time for your mind, body and soul.

What is Environmental Sustainability?

The term "sustainability" relates to the Earth and its natural ecosystems, and our ability as inhabitants on this Earth to preserve it for future generations. Its intent is that all of human life is able to meet its needs, while minimizing our footprint on the environment around us and preserving natural ecosystems for the long-term. Many believe that the Earth has been here forever and that there is little impact one family can have on it. That couldn't be farther from the truth! There is a great deal you can do to help preserve our planet, and, in doing so... you're teaching your children to respect the world we live in. Chances are, you're beginning a solid foundation that your children and grandchildren will pass to future generations.

1. There is indisputable evidence that our world is changing. Scientists know that our natural systems are declining, our climate is changing due to global warming and the Earth's natural energy sources are also declining. These changes affect our world today and threaten future generations. However, everyone, from the largest companies to families across America, can have a positive impact on the environment.

2. The average family spends about $1,300 on utilities each year, and much of that on heating and cooling their homes. Consider seeking ways to reduce your usage and your budget. Turn the thermostat down just 2 degrees in colder months and up 2 degrees in the summer. Many families are out of the home during the day. Consider a timer that automatically turns the heat up or down to use less energy throughout the day. Consider solar power as an alternative to natural gas or electricity.

3. Many homes are insulated with fiberglass insulation (a combination of mined substances and recycled glass). Consider using recycled cotton or cellulose insulation made of recycled newspapers, and readily available at many home stores.

4   Retail stores across the country are now carrying environmentally-friendly cleaning products and laundry detergents with all-natural ingredients – look for products with citrus-based oils to get the most cleaning power with the least environmental impact.

5   Reduce, Reuse, Recycle! Make recycling a daily routine in your home by separating aluminum cans, paper, cardboard, plastics and more, and participating in your community's recycling program. Many garbage companies, city governments and other organizations offer recycling bins that you can pick up for free to put your recyclables in at your home.

6   You can also recycle many other household items, such as old printer cartridges, cellular phones, computers, video tapes, eyeglasses, CDs and DVDs, batteries, Christmas trees, fluorescent light bulbs and carpets. Contact local recycling resources for more information about recycling these items or research the Internet for companies that will recycle these items for you.

7   You may already recycle at home, but what about in your office? Encourage your office to start a paper-recycling program, use both sides of the paper for non-essential items, put extra bins in the kitchen for cans and bottles only, or use reusable dishware in the cafeteria instead of disposables.

8   Many companies are using recyclable packaging and reducing packaging size to minimize their impact on the environment. Look for products that are "higher-concentrate" that use less packaging; and therefore, have less of an impact on the environment.

9   Replace toilets and appliances in your home with new systems that use less water, another precious resource.

10 Reduce the amount of time you travel by car, especially when you're alone. Consider using public transportation to get back and forth to work. Bundle errands together and drive to a central area and walk to minimize stopping and starting your car often. The good news is... not only are you helping preserve our natural resources... but, you're doing something healthy for yourself at the same time.

11 Preserve your "Personal Sustainability" by making a conscious effort to balance your own systems – physical, emotional and spiritual. Plan time for spiritual rejuvenation, fun with family and friends, and personal pampering.

Granola

"I scream, you scream, we all scream for ice cream!" So why not add to the "health experience" by adding some granola and fresh berries!

INGREDIENTS

1 1/2 cups	rolled oats
1/2 cup	oat flour
1/4 cup	cashews
1/2 cup	almonds
pinch	cinnamon
pinch	salt
2 Tbsp.	apple juice concentrate
1 Tbsp.	pineapple or orange juice concentrate
1/4 cup	light coconut milk
1 Tbsp.	brown sugar
1 Tbsp.	vanilla extract
3/4 tsp.	cashew butter
1 Tbsp.	maple syrup
1/4 cup	dried cranberries
3/4 cup	dried cherries
2 Tbsp.	honey, heated

Cook's Note:
Feel free to substitute almond butter or peanut butter for cashew butter.

You can make oat flour in the food processor from regular or quick rolled oats.

PREPARATION

- Preheat oven to 275 degrees. Lightly coat a sheet pan with canola oil.
- Combine oats, oat flour, nuts, cinnamon and salt in a medium bowl and mix well.
- Combine apple juice concentrate, pineapple juice concentrate, coconut milk, brown sugar, vanilla extract, cashew butter and maple syrup in a small bowl and mix well. Add to dry mixture and mix until ingredients are moist.
- Crumble mixture onto sheet pan and bake for 45 minutes to 1 hour, stirring after 25 minutes to allow for even cooking. Remove granola from oven, break apart while still slightly warm and add dried fruit and honey. Cool on sheet pan.

NUTRITIONAL ANALYSIS
Makes 12 (1/2 cup) servings. Each serving contains approximately:

200	calories
4 g.	protein
32 g.	carbohydrates
6 g.	fat
0 mg.	cholesterol
36 mg.	sodium
3 g.	fiber

*Mom was always beside me,
for assurance....*

Dear Mom,

...and love

It's been almost 3 years since you passed and there isn't a day that I don't think about you or wish you were here. The kids and the whole family miss you terribly.

We get together often with all our relatives. After the accident we made a commitment to stay close to each other. I know that having a sense of family was important to you as it is to all of us. I try to keep your memory alive by constantly telling stories, cooking great food and reinforcing the lessons that you taught me throughout my life.

You remain the most influential person in my life. I hope that I am as good a teacher to my kids as you were to me. You taught me that respect is the most important part of any relationship, especially self-respect. I tell the kids this often. I also tell them how important it is to do the right thing and that doing the right thing is sometimes hard. I tell them to have strength of character. Not a day goes by without some reference to "Boo Boo" and what you taught me.

You would be so proud of the kids. They are growing up so nicely. They are good students, fun, and most importantly, they are good people. Both Julia and John are taking Chinese. They have such a love and an interest in their heritage. We are excited to celebrate Chinese New Year this year and good news... Sweet O' and Baby Boo Boo are going to take your place at school. They will be making dumplings for the entire student body.

If you could come back for a day, I would love for you to spend that day with JD. He is a year and a half and such a character. It is too bad that you never got to hold him or talk to him. Hopefully you get a kick out of watching him from Heaven. I know Daddy does. He thinks that JD is you reincarnated.

Mom, I hope you are well. I know that you are looking after us. Thanks for being our guardian angel. We miss and love you so much.

XOXO,

Jeannine

PERSONAL SAFETY

It doesn't take a formal education for a Mom to know by intuition...

...how to protect her family. That is a gift from God. The good news is... Moms today can build on that intuition by learning safety tips from experts that can help us survive and flourish in our modern world.

Personal Safety

1. Trust your instincts. If your inner voice tells you to be cautious... do it! Better safe than sorry.

2. Keep your keys ready in your hand when walking to your house or car so that they are always ready to use.

3. Always lock the doors to your house and car, even if you are only leaving for a moment.

4. In the summer, keep your car windows up if possible. Use your air conditioner.

5. Always make eye contact and don't walk with your head down.

6. Before getting in your car, glance under and in it. After you unlock the door, close it firmly, lock your doors, buckle your seatbelt and drive away immediately. Any delays (adjusting items, putting in a CD, etc.) are moments that make you vulnerable to an attacker.

7. When possible, have someone else with you when you go out. When walking, be sure someone knows the route you're taking. If you walk regularly for exercise, take a friend or dog when possible. If going alone, vary your route and routine.

8. The most important weapon you have is your mind. Be smart by being aware of your surroundings.

Hotel Safety

1. Sign in using your first initial and last name only. Do not display your room key in public.

2. Before you open the door for room service, require them to slide the bill under the door.

3. Make sure your door locks properly. If not, request another room.

4. Use all safety locks when securing your door – not just the deadbolt. Deadbolts can still be "unlocked" by certain access cards from hotel security.

5. Make sure the balcony and adjoining room doors are securely locked.

6. Do not put your name on the outside of your luggage. Put a business card inside your suitcase and attach other items (a polka-dotted ribbon) to the outside to identify your luggage at baggage claim.

7. Display the "Do Not Disturb" sign on the door, whether or not you are in the room. Call housekeeping to arrange a convenient cleaning time.

8. Leave the TV or radio on and a bright light on when you leave the room.

9. Be sure to locate the nearest exits and know the route for an emergency exit in the event of a fire.

Family Safety

1. With your children, keep your "Mommy Radar" on at all times to see what could be a hazard and how to prevent accidents.

2. Do a "crawl through" of your home to see things from a child's perspective.

3. Be a role model – if you buckle up in a car or wear your helmet on a bike, children will notice and follow your example.

4. Teach your children to practice safe habits around animals, even if the animal belongs to someone they know. Tell your children to always ask permission from the owner before approaching an animal.

5. Talk to your children about safety – be sure they know how to dial 9-1-1 and know at least two ways to escape from the home if a fire starts. Have family fire drills once a year.

6. Talk to your child about how to avoid predators and abductors in person and online. Get to know your child's friends and their families. Don't allow your child to play at a friend's house unless you have met the family.

Divine Summertime Chicken Sandwich

When you're taking a day to pamper yourself, you'll surely enjoy having a wholesome, nutritious and eye-appealing lunch. Remember... it's all about you – and you are what you eat! Celebrate all that you are and want to be.

INGREDIENTS

2	skinless, boneless chicken breasts, cut in half
1 tsp.	garlic, minced
1 tsp.	olive oil
1/4 tsp.	salt
pinch	black pepper
3 oz.	cream cheese, softened
1 Tbsp.	red onion, minced
2 Tbsp.	fresh dill, chopped
2 Tbsp.	minced pimentos or roasted red peppers
4 slices	French bread, (1-inch thick)
4	lettuce leaves
4	tomato slices

NUTRITIONAL ANALYSIS
Makes 4 servings. Each serving contains approximately:

255	calories
21 g.	protein
26 g.	carbohydrates
8 g.	fat
48 mg.	cholesterol
444 mg.	sodium
4 g.	fiber

PREPARATION

- With a meat mallet, pound chicken breasts between 2 pieces of waxed paper to 1/2-inch thick. Season chicken breasts with salt and pepper.

- Heat olive oil in a medium sauté pan over medium heat. Add garlic and briefly sauté. Add chicken breasts and sauté for 3 to 5 minutes on each side or until the meat is firm and the juices run clear. Remove from pan and set aside.

- In a medium bowl, mix together the cream cheese, red onion, dill and pimento or roasted red peppers.

- Spread cream cheese mixture on all 4 slices of bread.

- Spray opposite side of bread with canola oil spray and toast in a large sauté pan for 30 seconds to 1 minute or until lightly browned.

- Place chicken, tomato slice and lettuce leaf on bread slice and serve.

Mom and her girls,
joined at the hip...

Dearest
Mother,

...with my fashion icon

...with my greatest gifts

I write this note to you in tribute and thanks for being the single biggest inspiration in my life and for being my very best friend. What a tremendous opportunity and privilege for me to honor you, Mom, in this way.

From the time I was a little girl, you have always instilled confidence in me and my abilities. You encouraged me to be the best I could be. You taught me to love God and family.

You inspired my creativity by setting such a great example, always surrounding your family in beauty and taking the time to point out the beauty in life, whether it was a magnificent sunset or simply the way a group of clouds took shape against the backdrop of green trees and blue skies.

I always admired your natural talent and eye for fashion. I think I always knew, instinctively, of your secret passion to be a designer. I guess it is not totally surprising that I chose the beauty industry to pursue my dreams, thanks to your encouragement and creative nurturing.

Mom, your intense love of family is one of the greatest gifts that you have instilled in each of your three daughters from the very beginning. I can always recall you telling us to take care of one another, and to be supportive of one another no matter what life brings. As you continue to remind us of this, even today, I also cherish your ability to find humor in most anything that comes our way. I remember you telling me, "Focus on the positive, not on the negative."

As for work ethic, you always taught us to never give up, to never take anything for granted, to have passion for what you do, to be relentless in whatever your pursuit and, most importantly, to believe in yourself and your ability to achieve anything you put your mind to.

Mom, you are and continue to be for me, Jane and Linda, our hero, our quintessential role model.

I thank you for your strength, your unconditional love, your many sacrifices, especially after Dad passed away. I thank you for giving me, Jane and Linda the wind to sail. And perhaps your greatest gift, I thank you for the blessing of showing us what it takes to be a great Mom.

With all my love and gratitude,

Your loving daughter,

Karen

BEAUTY

Most of us learned our first beauty secrets from our Mothers and Grandmothers.

Over the years, we've developed our own sense of style. Mom was right – it's true, "Beauty is as beauty does"... eat a healthy diet, exercise, count your blessings and try these ideas for overall beauty and confidence-building!

Makeup

1 Today's cosmetic choices include products formulated specifically for individual skin types – anti-aging, anti-acne, matte, creamy, powder and liquid.

2 Selecting the right foundation shade will present a more even, perfect coverage. Compare the shade to the skin along the jaw line for an ideal match.

3 No matter what your skin tone – African, Asian, Latin, European – many women do not make the correct color selections. For example, dark-skinned women may go too light and light-skinned women may go too dark. Many women find that mixing two shades together helps perfect the match.

4 Squeezing a small amount of foundation onto the back of your hand will help warm the foundation and allow for smooth application.

5 If you need extra coverage in problem areas, consider adding a concealer after you've applied your foundation. To counter darkness under the eyes, choose a shade with yellow undertones that is one or two shades lighter than your skin tone.

6 When choosing a blush, remember that common forms bond best. For example, if you are applying blush over a powdered face, choose a powdered blush. Use a creamy blush with a liquid foundation. If you pinch your cheeks, you will reveal your natural blush. Match this color for your most natural, flattering effect.

7 Many women love a bronzed, sun-kissed glow. Apply bronzer anywhere the sun naturally hits your face... the center of your forehead, tip of your nose, tops of your cheeks and chin. For evening, you can also use a bronzer to highlight your neck and collarbone.

8 Color selection is just as important when choosing cosmetics for eyes and lips. When choosing a lipstick, consider the color as it looks on your skin, not as it looks in the tube. A medium pink may appear intense and dramatic on a light-skinned woman, but may have a much more subtle effect on a dark-skinned woman.

9 A lip liner provides definition to the lip shape, acting as a "fence" to hold your lipstick in. Use a liner that's slightly darker than your lip color shade and blend it downward to cover your lips. This makes the line seem less harsh and produces a base coat to make your color last longer.

10 Consider using an eye pencil for greater definition. Outline the shape of your eye by drawing a line along the upper lash line beginning at the center of the eyelid and working outward.

11 When applying mascara, position the brush/comb as close to the base of your eyelid as possible. Start by coating the top of your lashes on the upper eyelid, then coat the bottom of those top lashes. Think of your lashes as having three sections. Be sure to apply mascara not just to the center but also to the inner and outer sections for maximum effect. Apply several coats to the bottom lashes to really make them noticeable.

Hair

1 Keep your hair shiny and clean with a shampoo and conditioner that are specially-formulated for your hair type – normal, oily, dry or sensitive. If hair is chemically-processed, use a deep conditioner or a leave-in conditioner once a week to restore its moisture.

2 When coloring your hair:

- Follow the color guide on the box to see what results you can expect for your hair color. The hair color on the front of the box will not always be the color you can expect.

- Make sure to follow every step in the directions to ensure the hair color you want.

- To ensure that the chosen color is right for you, use the "strand test." Color just a few strands to make sure you've chosen what you want.

- Keep your colored hair healthy by doing a root touch-up. Do not re-color your entire head each time. Apply product to roots only and set the rest of the product aside. Leave color on your roots for the full amount of time. Apply remaining color to the balance of your hair for the last 5 minutes only.

3 Never brush your hair when it is wet. This may lead to breakage. Use a wide-toothed comb to detangle. Brushes should be used only after hair has been dried.

A good night tip: make sure to use an eye makeup remover to remove shadow, liner and mascara. The skin around the eye is very delicate. Apply a soaked cotton pad to your eyelid for several seconds, then wipe gently downward.

Noni's Potato Pie

Noni's Potato Pies are a perfect example of a delicious everyday recipe that is "Yum, good enough for company!"

INGREDIENTS

2 lb.	red bliss potatoes
1/2 cup	buttermilk
1/2 cup	2% milk
1 Tbsp.	butter
1/2 tsp.	salt
1/2 tsp.	ground black pepper
2	whole eggs
8 oz.	low-fat mozzarella cheese, shredded
1/2 cup	Parmesan cheese, grated
1/2 lb.	diced all-natural ham free of nitrates and preservatives
2 Tbsp.	parsley, freshly chopped
3/4 cup	panko bread crumbs

NUTRITIONAL ANALYSIS
Makes 12 servings. Each serving contains approximately:

320	calories
22 g.	protein
30 g.	carbohydrates
12 g.	fat
99 mg.	cholesterol
750 mg.	sodium
5 g.	fiber

PREPARATION

- Preheat oven to 350 degrees. Lightly coat a 9"x13"x 2" baking pan with canola oil and dust with 1/4 cup of panko bread crumbs.

- Place 8 cups water in a large saucepan and bring to a boil. Add potatoes and cook for 10 to 15 minutes or until potatoes are tender. Turn off heat and drain water.

- With an electric mixer add milks, butter, salt and black pepper. Mix until all ingredients are mixed well.

- Turn mixer to low and add eggs followed by cheeses, ham and parsley.

- Pour potato mixture into pan and top with remaining 1/2 cup of panko bread crumbs. Bake in a 350 degree oven for 45 minutes. Cut into 12 servings and serve with 1/2 cup fresh vegetables or 2 cups green salad.

Note: For a special dinner party, substitute a cupcake tin for the baking pan to create individual servings.

P.S. For easy removal, use cupcake liners coated with non-stick cooking spray.

Dear
Mom,

Ginger, our favorite
"Spice Girl,"
and her family

Ginger and her beloved Mom

Boy, do I miss you!!

Your name comes up all the time in conversations with family, friends, business associates and acquaintances. When family events are planned, we discuss how much you would have enjoyed them. If someone is in need, we mention what you would have done to reach out with food, clothing and a shoulder to lean on – and because you would have done something, we try to also. It seems we often remark about how hard you worked, how much you helped others and how much joy you expressed in the "doing."

I quote you a lot, too. I'm practicing answering questions affirmatively, like you always did for me. When I asked, "Mom, could you do this for me?" You answered, "Absolutely!" Now I understand the power of that word! It offered complete support and affirmation; never a hint that I had imposed or you had other more important things to do. Simple and energetic support – thank you for that gift.

When the challenge seems too difficult or the task too great, I hear you asking, "What's the worst that could happen?" And it's usually not that bad, so I just go for it.

In those times when life seems overwhelming and weighing me down, I hear you whisper, "Don't sweat the small stuff." And I make choices and move on, focused anew on how blessed I am.

Your life was so different than mine, but you brought your values to your role as parent. Through the Dust Bowl and the Great Depression, you learned to be frugal and resourceful. You taught me to save my money and make my own clothes. While you kept the books at the local Ford Motor Company, you taught me to foot columns and rows so that I was "good at numbers." While you ran a catering business, you taught me how to entertain with grace and beauty. And you helped me understand that it doesn't matter how much money a person makes, their manners tell you who they really are. That was one of your greatest gifts to me. As you worked side-by-side with Dad on the farm, you two showed me how to treasure life, be respectful of death and persevere. I know the hard work involved in growing your own food and the importance of cultivating a flower garden along side the crops that would feed us: Those flowers fed our soul. As you cared for elderly neighbors and stepped in at times of local tragedy, you taught us about community and responsibility. As kids, through manual labor we learned the power of self-esteem earned through accomplishment and how to survive failures: You picked yourself up and tried again.

I have dozens of your cake pans, piles of cook books and boxes of recipes. Mostly, I have your recipe for life: Work hard, serve others and be joyful.

I love you, Mom.

Ginger

DIABETES

Even though genetics may play a role in developing diabetes,

you can be empowered to make simple changes to live a "sweet" life. Share this information with your Mom, your Daughters and other women whom you love and cherish.

Risk Factors

You may not know it, but, you're not alone. Nearly 55 million women have a condition called pre-diabetes, and may have no symptoms at all. If you have pre-diabetes, you have a very high chance of getting type 2 diabetes. More than a quarter of the people with type 2 diabetes don't know they have it. That's why it's particularly important to pay attention to the signs and symptoms of diabetes and its risk factors and to get tested if you are at risk.

Signs & Symptoms

1. Age, ethnicity, being overweight, lack of physical activity and family history all play a role in the development of diabetes.

2. Find out if anyone in your family has or had a history of diabetes. Even with a family history, you can often prevent this disease with lifestyle changes.

3. The symptoms of diabetes may begin gradually and are often difficult to identify. Some of the signs of diabetes are:
   - feeling thirsty most of the time
   - frequent urination and having to urinate during the night
   - feeling very hungry or tired
   - weight loss or gain, without trying
   - sores that heal slowly
   - dry, itchy skin
   - tingling or loss of feeling in your feet
   - blurred vision

4. If you are pregnant, gestational diabetes is also a risk to your health. Non-diabetic pregnant women should be checked for diabetes between the 24th and 28th week of pregnancy, unless they are in a low-risk category. Low risk includes women who have no family history of diabetes, are of normal weight and are younger than 25 years of age. See Chapter 8 for more information on a healthy pregnancy.

Detection

1   All adults age 45 and older should be tested for diabetes every 3 years. For higher-risk women, testing should begin at a younger age and should be done more frequently.

2   Know the ABCs of diabetes to live a long and healthy life – "A" is for A1C test, which measures your average blood glucose (sugar) over the last 3 months; "B" is for blood pressure, suggested target is below 130/80; "C" is for cholesterol, lower your total cholesterol below 200 for ideal health.

3   To test for diabetes, blood samples are drawn after you have swallowed a sugary solution. If your glucose levels are higher than normal, it's possible your pancreas isn't producing enough insulin, increasing your risk for diabetes.

4   Keep your medical appointments faithfully. A critical part of detecting and controlling diabetes is regular medical examinations.

Spice up your life! Some studies suggest that adding cinnamon to your hot tea, coffee or toast each day may improve your body's ability to use insulin.

Prevention

Managing pre-diabetes (and preventing type 2 diabetes) requires lifestyle changes, namely eating healthier and increasing your physical activity. According to Lisa Porter, M.D., endocrinologist, "It's the combination of diet and exercise that make a difference… one without the other is not nearly as effective."

1   Get up and move! Regular physical activity is also a protective factor against diabetes. It lowers your blood pressure and builds a healthy heart. Include the three components of a comprehensive fitness program: strength training, cardiovascular exercises and flexibility.

2   Control your weight and reduce the fat in your diet to reduce your risk. The good news is… a diet low in fat and moderate in calories also helps keep you healthy overall.

3   Increase the amount of whole grains, fruits and vegetables you eat. Learn how to prepare healthy foods without excess sugar or fats.

4   Excess weight carried above the waist is a stronger risk factor for diabetes and heart disease than excess weight carried below the waist.

Crescent Rolls

Whether it's down on the farm or in the middle of a busy urban area, this recipe for classic crescent rolls will send your family over the moon!

INGREDIENTS

- 1 yeast cake or 1 pkg. dry yeast, softened in 3 Tbsp. warm water
- 3 eggs, beaten
- 1 cup warm water
- ½ cup sugar
- 1 tsp. salt
- 1 stick melted butter
- 5 cups flour

PREPARATION

- Mix all ingredients, cover, and let stand overnight. Next day, divide dough into quarters and roll out to ⅛-inch thickness.
- Cut into triangles and brush with butter.
- Roll up and let stand 3-5 hours on cookie sheets.
- Bake at 375 degrees for 8-12 minutes.

***May be placed in freezer and rewarmed in microwave.**

This is not a Canyon Ranch makeover recipe.

NUTRITIONAL ANALYSIS
Makes 24 servings. Each serving contains approximately:

155	calories
4 g.	protein
25 g.	carbohydrates
5 g.	fat
36 mg.	cholesterol
88 mg.	sodium
1 g.	fiber

Off and running...

...but never far away

A true gift

One of the greatest gifts I have ever received, is a gift I received from my Mom. "To be the best that she can be, a woman needs not only to educate herself and give 100% to whatever she does, but she needs to take chances," I heard my Mom say to me many times when I was just a teenager. She then did something that had to be the hardest thing a Mother can do: she set me free.

The second of five children, I was brought up in Puerto Rico in a tight-knit family. Our house was always busy. School night hours were filled with sports, music lessons, homework, family dinner every single night. And orchestrating all the instruments to come together like a flawless musical composition was Mami, my Mother. Get one kid from ballet, drop off the other one's basketball uniform at the school, attend the PTA meeting, stop by Abuela's house. She nurtured our creativity, nursed us when we were under the weather, picked us up when we failed and cheered us from the sidelines when we did something good. To be the wife, the Mother, the daughter, the friend, and as she would say "the cook, the driver, the hostess..." and to keep it all in balance, wasn't easy. Needless to say, she wasn't perfect. But to me she was.

At the end of the day, after her whole world had revolved around us and she had made little time for her things, she still managed to teach me another great lesson: that a good Mother also needs to take care of herself.

Fast forward a few years, and five kids slowly grew up. Mom's advice was always the same: "go to school, get a career, find happiness..." And one by one, she set each one of us free, on the path to the opportunities that only a good education could bring. She knew that distance was something that she would just have to get used to, or better yet work with. She took a chance by letting us go.

It is that freedom Mom gave me and the love and support that I feel from the distance that I am most thankful for. Had it not been for that, I would not be who I am today. I can only hope that my three children would find me to be the inspiration my Mother has been to me.

¡Gracias Mami!

Johanna

VITAMINS & MINERALS

Cod liver oil? Yuk! But... wait!

Doesn't the latest medical research show that taking fish oil can improve our overall health and well-being? So, Mom was right... thank goodness fish oil now comes in capsules! Researchers are learning more every day about the advantages of vitamins, minerals and other daily essentials. Learn what you can do to enhance your physical, emotional and mental well-being.

A healthy lifestyle begins with healthy food choices. The more you know about the fuel you put in your precious machine, the better choices you will be able to make.

Good-For-You Foods

1   Eat a rainbow of colors. The more intense the colors of your fruits and vegetables, the more vitamins, minerals and antioxidants they provide. Think tomatoes, dark leafy greens, carrots and blueberries.

2   To add a bit of Vitamin C to your daily diet, add a splash of lemon juice to your water. Vitamin C boosts your immune system, helps the body take in iron and is a gentle liver cleanser.

3   Go nuts! All nuts are full of fiber, protein, mainly good fats, Vitamin E, copper (which is great for your heart) and magnesium. Almonds also contain calcium and walnuts have Omega-3s. But, eat them in moderation. About 10 nuts is considered a healthy serving.

4   Lentils, beans and other legumes are low in fat and high in protein. They can also moderate your blood pressure and send that LDL (think "L" for "Lousy") cholesterol level down.

5   A 4-ounce portion of Omega-3 rich fish like salmon and other coldwater fish, eaten at least twice a week, will help reduce the risk of heart disease and certain types of cancer.

6   Soy provides antioxidant powers and is a low-fat protein source. Consider using soy milk on your cereal, for cooking your oatmeal and in your smoothies. Add black soy beans to any dish that would use regular black beans. The benefits include healthier bones, less risk of heart disease and certain types of cancer. Soy contains isoflavones, which may assist in reducing the effects of hot flashes and improve cholesterol and blood sugar levels. If you have estrogen-receptive cancers, consult your health care provider about the amount of soy you should be eating.

7. "Organic" food is produced according to organic standards. They commonly include food grown without the use of pesticides or fertilizers, animals raised without routine use of antibiotics or growth hormones, and food processed without use of radiation or food additives. This food is not genetically engineered in any way.

Vitamins & Minerals

1. So what is the difference between vitamins and minerals? Vitamins are organic substances (made by plants or animals). Minerals are inorganic substances that come from soil and water and are absorbed by plants or eaten by animals. Your body needs differing amounts of vitamins and minerals to survive (lots of calcium, Vitamin C, etc.). However, other vitamins and minerals are called trace elements (iron, magnesium, copper, etc.) because we only need a small amount of them every day. Note: magnesium has been reported to ease leg and foot cramping. Consider a slow-release formula.

2. Vitamins and minerals help boost the immune system, support normal growth and development, and help cells and organs function. Eating right during crucial times in life like childhood, puberty, pregnancy and menopause is essential to make sure we are getting all of the vitamins and minerals we need.

Many people wonder if they should be taking vitamin or mineral supplements. If your diet has a wide variety of foods, you are probably already getting the vitamins and minerals your body needs. Consult with a health care professional, dietitian or pharmacist to talk about your need for vitamin or mineral supplements.

3. If you are a vegan or vegetarian, you'll need to plan to make sure you get all of the vitamins and minerals you need, as plants do not provide all of the essential vitamins and minerals. Vitamin B_{12}, which is important for making red blood cells, is not found in plants. Zinc and iron are primarily found in meats, fish and poultry. Consult with a dietitian when planning your vegetarian lifestyle.

Black Bean Salad

This Black Bean Salad contains lots of good-for-you ingredients, including foods that are high in fiber and "good" fats. You might want to use some of these table decorations to delight your family and guests.

INGREDIENTS

Salad

1	fresh diced avocado
2 lbs.	frozen corn
15 oz.	canned black beans, rinsed
1 cup	fresh chopped scallions
1¼ cups	diced red peppers
2 cups	fresh chopped tomatoes
2	jalapeno peppers

Salad Dressing

½ cup plus 2 Tbsp.	lime juice
½ cup	chopped cilantro
2 Tbsp.	olive oil
1 Tbsp.	granulated sugar
1 tsp.	minced garlic
1 tsp.	dried oregano
2 tsp.	salt
¼ tsp.	black pepper

PREPARATION

- Preheat oven to 375 degrees.
- In a small bowl, combine all ingredients for salad dressing.
- Add the diced avocado to the dressing, toss gently, and set aside.
- On a large sheet pan, roast the corn in the oven for 20 – 25 minutes, or until slightly golden. Add the corn to a medium bowl and chill in the refrigerator.
- In a large bowl, combine chilled corn, black beans, scallions, red peppers, tomatoes and jalapenos. Toss with dressing.

NUTRITIONAL ANALYSIS
Makes 16 servings. Each serving contains approximately:

130	calories
5 g.	protein
21 g.	carbohydrates
4 g.	fat
0 mg.	cholesterol
245 mg.	sodium
5 g.	fiber

Always a smile

*Pink worked for
my Mom and me...*

...and for Celia

I'm Cathy Kilbane, and I'm the Senior Vice President & General Counsel of American Greetings Corporation. I'm also the very proud Mother of Celia, age 3, and the Daughter of Judy Robertson. When Mom was 34 and I was 13, my Father died, leaving Mom to raise four children, me being the oldest.

My Mother re-entered the workforce as a secretary and for many years juggled motherhood with the demands of a career. She retired as a manager from IBM and now spends her time as a community volunteer, avid bridge player and Grandma extraordinaire to Celia and her other grandkids.

I would've written my Mom a letter, but she and I are both more familiar with "to-do" lists.

TOP 10 THINGS I LEARNED FROM MY MOM
By Cathy Kilbane

1. Finding joy in the chaos of a crowded kitchen table.
2. Great Halloween costumes can be made of a pillowcase and magic markers.
3. A sense of humor is an essential life skill.
4. My Daughter doesn't care if the dishes sit in the sink while I help her make a pizza out of Play Doh.
5. My career should be my second favorite job.
6. Graciousness in the face of tragedy, determination in the face of adversity.
7. A vacation means someone else cooks.
8. Celebrate, really celebrate, occasions for joy.
9. A station wagon can be its own fashion statement.
10. Great Moms make extraordinary Grandmas.

Cathy

GREAT RELATIONSHIPS

One of life's first relationships is with our Mothers.

As you will see, so many of the love notes to Moms shared in this book talk about how Daughters learned from their Moms the art of mothering, raising happy children and establishing loving relationships. Do you recognize any of the words of wisdom in this chapter for maintaining healthy, loving relationships?

Being a Good Friend

1. Be the kind of friend you'd like to have. Set an example for others and, chances are, they'll return the favor in kind.

2. Be of service. You've been blessed with a bounty of talents and gifts, so share them with the world by way of volunteering, making financial contributions or just extending yourself to those less fortunate than you.

3. Be responsible for your own mental, physical, emotional and spiritual health. All of your relationships will suffer if you are not taking care of yourself. Self-care is the prerequisite for healthy relating.

4. Avoid misusing friends as therapists or banks. It's OK to turn to a friend for occasional emotional support or even letting them pick up the lunch tab now and then, but make sure you reciprocate.

5. Respect your friends' boundaries, especially if you've been "Friends Forever." There may come a time where your friend (or you) may want to withhold certain intimate details or topics about her life (or your life) that you shared quite freely before marriage/children, etc. That's OK and it does not mean you're not still close and caring friends.

Resolving Conflicts

1. Pay attention to your communication style. When you feel or think you are misunderstood, simply consider that the other person may prefer a different way of hearing what you say.

2. When a rift in one of your relationships happens, begin with yourself. Is there anything going on inside you that could create that rift?

3. Learn to say "I'm sorry," and more importantly, learn to forgive – one another and yourself. Be observant regarding your ability to forgive.

4 Take the first step. Mending a broken relationship often requires that one person makes the first call. Don't let days, weeks or even months pass before you address the problem.

5 A common problem in any relationship is transferring feelings of anger to our loved ones when we're really angry at someone or something else. Try to pinpoint exactly what it is that's bothering you and not let it affect your relationships.

Communicating

1 As with everything in a relationship, communication is key. Choose a time to discuss your issues when both parties can focus, are not distracted and when the timing is right.

2 In all relationships, listen carefully, sympathetically and with empathy. Be responsive to what your friend or loved one is sharing, not just thinking about what you want to say next.

3 Make time for talking to and getting together with your friends. Being busy too often and for too extended a period may result in fading or ending those relationships. If you are busy now, or will be in the foreseeable future, try to agree on a specific plan for getting together with your friend or loved one and commit to it.

4 Observe yourself in various situations – especially at home and at work. Where are you and others alike and different? Instead of trying to change others, use these differences to learn more about yourself.

Reaping Health Benefits

1 Value your connections and recognize that relationships increase the health of women.

2 Assure adequate nutrition. Continue to regularly feed your relationships with proper nutrients: love, laughter, hugs, compassion, communication and prayer. Your endorphins will reward you!

3 The best relationships are those that don't take themselves too seriously. Friends who laugh together, stay together!

4 Frequent connections with good friends and family can have a huge impact on your physical well-being, as well. They can actually boost your immune system!

Chicken Posole

S ay "Hola!" to this heart-healthy Chicken Posole.

INGREDIENTS

2 tsp.	canola oil
1½ lbs.	skinless chicken breast, boned and defatted, cut into cubes
1 Tbsp.	garlic, minced
1	small onion, peeled and diced
¼ cup	diced green chili
4 cups	canned hominy, drained
1 Tbsp.	chili powder
1 tsp.	coriander powder
1 tsp.	cumin powder
1 tsp.	dried oregano
¼ tsp.	black pepper
1 tsp.	paprika
2 tsp.	salt
2 quarts	chicken stock
1 quart	vegetable stock

Suggested Garnish

¾ cup	thinly sliced radish
1½ cups	shredded cabbage
1½ cups	thinly sliced onion
2 Tbsp.	chopped cilantro
1	lime, cut into 6 wedges
6 Tbsp.	tomato, diced
6 Tbsp.	Anaheim chiles, diced

PREPARATION

- In a large sauce pan, heat canola oil. Add chicken and sear on outside. Add garlic, onions and green chilies and sauté briefly. Add remaining ingredients except for garnish (radish, cabbage, onion, cilantro and lime wedge). Bring to a boil, reduce heat and simmer 1 hour.

- Portion 1½ cups chicken posole into a bowl. Garnish with 2 Tbsp. sliced radish, ¼ cup cabbage, ¼ cup onion, 1 Tbsp. diced tomato, 1 Tbsp. diced Anaheim chile, 1 tsp. cilantro and 1 lime wedge. Repeat for remaining servings.

Cook's Note:
Another option for a garnish... try adding chopped tomatoes, 1 sliced black olive and diced jalapeno peppers to your Chicken Posole.

NUTRITIONAL ANALYSIS
Makes 6 servings. Each serving contains approximately:

365	calories
43 g.	protein
29 g.	carbohydrates
9 g.	fat
108 mg.	cholesterol
763 mg.	sodium
8 g.	fiber

Mom had...
a sense of humor,
a sense of business,
a sense of "what's right"

This legacy lives on in my Daughter

My Mother wasn't the traditional Mother of the 50's and 60's. She worked in business with my father and after their divorce, she worked outside the home and my brothers and I became "latch key kids," although that term didn't exist then. Mom was an incredibly hard worker with a great sense of humor and I like to think I possess both those traits.

We lived in several different states while I was growing up and there was no ethnic or religious intolerance allowed in our home. People were accepted for who they were – not for the color of their skin or religious affiliation. We could question our "elders" but we could not be disrespectful, good etiquette was a requisite – definitely no elbows on the dinner table – and using incorrect grammar or slang resulted in a fine, usually a quarter, which was big money then. Mother was loved by children and animals; instinctively, they trusted her. She was incredibly beautiful and fashionable during good times and bad. If she couldn't afford a knit suit, she knitted her own. I used to style her long black hair in a French twist, something she couldn't do herself. She's been gone 10 years and I still miss talking to her, sharing my successes and the messes I've made. As strong as she was, she couldn't kick the smoking habit and it eventually killed her. Mom (Patricia Belle) was the best Mother she could be. Her Mother died when she was 3 and female role-models were in short supply. She influenced my life in a very positive way.

Fondly,

Roxanne

EXERCISING

Benefits

1 We've always talked about fun activity and exercise as a core for optimal health. Recent research shows that even moderate exercise is as beneficial as intense workouts. Walking for 30 minutes a day (either all together or broken up into 3 sets of 10 minute walks) is just as beneficial as an intense cardio workout.

2 And now... a new study of more than 200,000 women suggests that doing household chores like dusting, mopping and vacuuming may help protect against cancer. While it's long been known that physical exercise lowers the risk of breast cancer – this study shows that moderate physical activity, like housework, may be more effective in reducing a woman's risk of breast cancer than more rigorous, but less frequent exercise. So, whether you're a career woman, a busy Mom or both... put a smile on your face, get out the mop and vacuum and go for it!

3 Physical activity includes more than just sit-ups and push-ups! Health experts say that laughter is actually a great exercise. Laughing 15 minutes burns the same amount of calories as 10 minutes of sit-ups. Do double duty – call a friend and meet for a walk. Chances are you'll find something to laugh about while walking together!

Get Motivated

1 Make a plan for yourself, outlining your daily and weekly goals. Better yet, all you need is a calendar, some gold stars and a goal. Every time you do something to reach that goal, put up a gold star. You'll be surprised how fast you attain it.

2 Healthy exercise is all about building healthy habits. You can't make exercise a habit if you aren't doing things you enjoy – choose an activity that will make you enjoy being active.

3   Two really is better than one! Find an exercise partner to help you achieve your fitness goals. When you don't feel like getting up in the morning to exercise, you will, because your exercise partner is depending on you and vice versa. An exercise partner can be a wonderful motivator.

4   Follow the 5-minute rule. If you don't feel like exercising, put on your shoes, go out the front door and walk around the block so you're back at your door in 5 minutes. If after 5 minutes, you're exhausted, stop... your body needs rest more than exercise. However, 9 times out of 10, you'll actually feel better, and this 5 minutes might expand to 10, 20 or even an hour.

5   Leave your exercise equipment out. Lean your bicycle against the side of your car. Put your tennis shoes on your front door step. Put hand weights in your kitchen. If you begin to see your exercise equipment, then one day, you'll actually use it!

Get Ready

1   Make sure you're dressed for success. Get workout clothes that fit and are made of fabrics that wick away sweat from your body. You should feel comfortable and your clothing should not restrict your movement in any way.

2   You should also wear comfortable shoes. Ill-fitting shoes can cause leg and foot pain. Replace shoes that are worn and no longer provide adequate support.

As you age, good balance becomes as important as flexibility, strength and cardio-respiratory fitness. Balance helps prevent the fall that fractures the hip. Try doing Tai chi to improve your balance. Even simple things like not stepping on sidewalk cracks or brushing your teeth on one foot can help build balance.

Mix It Up

1   Try using exercise bands as an alternative to hand weights. These are lightweight, portable, wide bands that distribute force evenly, helping to build muscle strength.

2   Make sure you stay hydrated during your workout. The American College of Sports Medicine suggests fluid before, during and after exercise to stay hydrated. If you exercise for more than 60 minutes, you may benefit from a sports drink containing carbohydrates.

3   Make the most of your time. Are you at your child's sports practices every week? Why not make laps around the field or hit the treadmill at the gym where your kids have swim class.

4   Stretch often, and in small doses. A few minutes of gentle stretching every day will be more effective than a full hour of Yoga or a stretch class done infrequently.

Snickerdoodles

Baking cookies and selling them can be a great start to life as an entrepreneur... in fact, some colleges and "first job" interviews include that question, "Did you ever have a lemonade stand?"

INGREDIENTS

¼ cup	butter
⅓ cup	low-fat cream cheese
1 cup	packed brown sugar
2	egg yolks
1 tsp.	vanilla extract
1 cup	all-purpose flour
⅓ cup	whole-wheat flour
1 tsp.	baking soda
¼ tsp.	cinnamon
½ tsp.	salt
5 Tbsp.	cinnamon sugar

PREPARATION

- Preheat oven to 350 degrees. Lightly coat a baking sheet with canola oil.

- In a large mixing bowl, mix butter, cream cheese and brown sugar on low speed with an electric mixer. Add egg yolk and vanilla and mix on low until just combined.

- In a medium bowl, combine remaining ingredients. Add to butter mixture and mix by hand until combined.

- Portion heaping teaspoonfuls (or use a ¾ oz. scoop) onto baking sheet about 1½-inches apart. Sprinkle lightly with cinnamon sugar. Bake for 7 minutes. Lightly flatten cookies with finger. Rotate baking sheet and bake an additional 3 minutes.

NUTRITIONAL ANALYSIS
Makes 30 cookies. Each cookie contains approximately:

80	calories
1 g.	protein
13 g.	carbohydrates
3 g.	fat
20 mg.	cholesterol
82 mg.	sodium
	trace fiber

Maya, Nick and me – a wonderful collaboration

My Dear Maya Angelou,

My treasured woman of influence

It's like I've always known you. As you sometimes say, "I can't remember when you weren't in my life." I will always be grateful to George Faison, director, choreographer and my friend for bringing Nick and me to your home in North Carolina for Thanksgiving so many years ago. It was love at first sight – and so comfortable and right. My natural Mother passed away at 57 years young and there's been a tremendous void I didn't think could be filled, but I've been so blessed to learn life lessons from you.

You have been so generous with your time and teaching – it's been like going to a university but so much more fun. The laughter and the stories you tell, color my thinking and make me realize how important it is to share this journey of life openly with those you love. I am so much braver now about being put on the spot and speaking at any time as a result of those round-table talks. As you always say, "Courage is the most important virtue because without it you can't practice any of the others consistently." Thank you for courage.

I know that you are the one I go to when times are good and when times are bad. Thank you for allowing me to feel free to express the hurt and the pain from the deepest places inside. I also know that my confidences are safe with you and you are placing me under your umbrella of prayer. That gives me great comfort and a peace that really sustains me. I remember one time in particular when as a Mother myself, I was confused as to how to be of the most help to my own Daughter – you were there for me and ready to fly to my side as an anchor.

You once told me, "Only equals make friends." So I count myself very fortunate, indeed, to have you as a supporter whether I'm writing a new song or working on a play or getting ready to perform at a new place. Whatever I'm doing, you embrace and push me forward. I know many would not think as a professional I would need encouragement but you know the child in each of us is always there.

I particularly love when you finish a new poem and before it's even off of your yellow pad – you give me a reading on the phone. How special that is to me! Nick always says, "There are some Angels right here on Earth." We know you are definitely one – so being around you puts us in that rarified air – what a blessing!!

Love you,

Valerie

LIFE BALANCE

Although it was invisible to us as children, our Moms were expert jugglers.

They kept all the balls in the air and if they were really smart, laughed when one dropped. Learn to do the same, and the young people in your life will tell wonderful stories about you.

Between work, family responsibilities, running errands, volunteering and everything else on your "to-do" list, you can find life balance. To create a sense of happiness and well-being, use these life balance notes as a guide.

Defining Happiness

1 There are four contributors to true happiness and balance – Control (including self-control), Optimism, Meaningful Activity and Personal Relationships.

2 When you invite balance into your life, you inevitably help those around you find balance in theirs. If others around you are happy and balanced, you will reap those rewards in return.

Making Time for You

1 Start bringing balance into your life by prioritizing what is most important. Talk to your family and loved ones. Many women are surprised to learn that completing everything on their to-do list is not necessarily what matters most to others.

2 Ask what "balance" means to you: How do you spend your time? What do you value? What are two of the most important areas you'd like to enhance or improve in your life? What are at least four things you can do to make those changes a reality?

3 Many women consider themselves to be "in charge" of everything. Chances are you feel overwhelmed when you're the only one planning, shopping, running errands and preparing meals. Consider establishing a Mom's night off – allow your children to prepare meals while you spend some time reading. Ask your partner to do laundry while you take a bubble bath. Don't feel guilty for spending some well-earned time on yourself!

4 Do something every day for 30 minutes that will help you become a better person. Read good books, listen to motivational tapes or consider listening to classical music.

5 In the midst of caring for everyone else, don't forget to keep yourself healthy too! This includes regularly exercising, eating balanced meals, getting plenty of rest and spending quality time with your friends and loved ones.

Taking the Right Approach

1. Dream big – realize your power within. If you can conceive the thought in your mind and believe it in your heart, then you can achieve it in your life.

2. Discover your unique purpose and "live on purpose." Every day, take time to look into your heart to understand who you are and where you're going.

3. Wise women know there is family by blood and by love. Treat them equally.

4. Maintain a forgiving spirit to achieve balance. First, forgive yourself and then forgive others. Forgiveness is for your empowerment and healing.

5. Listen to your instincts on your pathway to balance. There are times to take the knowledge and experiences that you have acquired and "go with your gut." Learn to trust your wise self.

6. Balance your life by the four-square method: self-care and self-fulfillment, family and friends, work and service, and tending to your mind, heart and spirit. The balance will never be perfect, but by concentrating on one of these every day, things work out in a more harmonious balance than we might have imagined.

7. One of the best-kept secrets of health and happiness is sharing laughter with those you love. Get a case of the giggles with girlfriends and be goofy with your family. Humor builds relationships, strengthens communication, invites balance and eases tension. Sharing moments of fun and laughter is a lifelong memory-maker.

8. Let go and streamline your life. Clear away the excess – every day define the essentials of what you need to live by to live with joy. Let go of the rest.

> **Give up the need to be "perfect." To invite balance into your life, celebrate the little things you have done well each day.**

Ashford Salad

The only cooking I do is on the piano... so I offer to you Maya Angelou's recipe for a salad created especially for Nick Ashford, my husband, taken from her cookbook *"Hallelujah! The Welcome Table."*

INGREDIENTS

2 heads	Romaine lettuce, with tough outer leaves removed
4 Tbsp.	extra-virgin olive oil
3 Tbsp.	fresh lemon juice
2 Tbsp.	red wine vinegar
1 Tbsp.	sugar
2 cloves	garlic, finely minced
	salt and freshly ground black pepper, to taste
1	ripe avocado, peeled and diced
1 large	ripe tomato, cut into small wedges
1 large	English cucumber, sliced

This is not a Canyon Ranch makeover recipe.

PREPARATION

- Wash lettuce, dry, wrap in paper towels and put into refrigerator.
- In large salad bowl, mix oil, lemon juice, vinegar, sugar and garlic.
- Season with salt and pepper.
- Mix in tomato and cucumber.
- Just before serving, remove lettuce from refrigerator, break into large pieces and toss in salad bowl.
- With salad tongs, mix vigorously until each lettuce leaf has been flavored with dressing.

NUTRITIONAL ANALYSIS
Makes 8 servings. Each serving contains approximately:

100	calories
1 g.	protein
6 g.	carbohydrates
9 g.	fat
0 mg.	cholesterol
122 mg.	sodium
2 g.	fiber

*With the wink of an eye
and an encouraging smile...*

...a coach

Dear Mom,

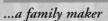

...a family maker

...a fantastic Mom

"Rise and Shine" is how you used to wake us up every morning – and that's exactly what comes to mind as I think of how you shaped and continue to shape my life. You always encouraged us to take action (Rise) and do our best (Shine) everyday.

As the youngest of three kids – all a year a part, you taught me to stand up for and believe in myself by letting me know that you were there, but that I had to figure things out on my own. With the wink of an eye and your encouraging smile, I knew when I was on the right track (and when I wasn't). You built my character one day at a time – so deep that "I never question who I am or where I came from." You are and always have been a cheerleader, a teacher, a coach, a mentor, a tradition keeper, a family maker and, most of all, a fantastic Mom.

You taught me the importance of traditions like having the same family dinner and opening gifts on Christmas Eve and then hanging out and enjoying the family on Christmas Day (made better by your famous casserole). When you and Dad moved from our "growing up" house after 30 years just before Christmas, it didn't matter, because all of the traditions you had built over the years were tied to us – not the house. When I walked down the aisle last year to marry the man of my dreams, I carried with me all the love that I learned by watching you (with us, Dad, your parents and many others) all these years.

No matter where I am in the world or what I'm doing, I walk with my head held high knowing that I have you behind me and as a part of me – always. THANK YOU for teaching and encouraging me to "Rise and Shine!" Know that your tireless and generous giving of YOU and all your love and wisdom is deeply seeded in your children. And, that's what I hope to pass along to my children someday. Most of all, I can't wait to watch them experience your "Rise and Shine" gifts firsthand.

I love you,

STRONG BONES

No bones about it... our Moms built the foundation for our lives.

When Mom told us to drink our milk, do our household chores and go outside and play... she was establishing our strong bones. This solid foundation can help us prevent osteoporosis as we age.

By age 25, the average woman has acquired 98% of her skeletal mass. Building strong bones during childhood and adolescence can be the best defense against developing osteoporosis later. The good news is... even after age 25, you can still take steps to prevent and treat osteoporosis.

Detection

1. Osteoporosis is a silent disease – you can have it and not know it because you can't feel your bones thinning. If you are at least 50 years old and female, you need to have a baseline bone density test.

2. Talk with your doctor about the results of your bone density test and be sure that you understand the health of your bones. A DXA scan is the most common and the "gold standard" for detecting osteoporosis.

3. Know Your T-Score! Your T-Score is a measurement from a bone density test that can help determine bone strength and the bones that have a potential for breaking. A T-Score of −1.0 or better indicates normal bone mass, while a score of −1.1 or worse indicates low bone mass and an increased risk of osteoporosis.

Nutrients

1. Your bones are definitely not a hard, lifeless foundation. They are complex living tissues made of calcium and protein that are constantly remodeling.

2. Post-menopausal women need at least 1200 mg of calcium each day in divided doses. Consider adding a supplement if you don't get enough with your diet alone. If you take a supplement, remember that your body can only absorb 600 mg of calcium at a time... so take a dose in the morning and at night instead of all at once.

3. Nature's bounty provides calcium-rich foods too! Include low-fat dairy products and green, leafy vegetables, such as broccoli, kale and spinach greens, cereals and breads fortified with calcium, sardines, turnips, almonds and salmon.

4. Women over age 50 need at least 400-800 IU of Vitamin D every day. This helps your body absorb calcium and may aid in preventing other diseases.

Prevention

1. Along with diet, exercise is a key building block to healthier bones. Look for the "Key 3" exercises to build strong bones at www.speakingofwomenshealth.com.

2. Keep active! Weight-bearing and strength-training exercises several times a week will keep your bones strong.

3. Avoid habits like smoking or excessive alcohol consumption – these can weaken the health of your bones.

4. Broken bones are a big deal. More women will die this year from the complications of osteoporosis (thinning bones are more likely to break) than from breast, ovarian and uterine cancers combined.

5. Prevent falls at home by eliminating problems that can cause them. Slippery floors can be replaced with rugs. Make sure these rugs adhere to the floor, and tuck away loose phone and electrical cords. Be sure all handrails are secured and add a railing in the shower if needed.

Risk Factors

1. If you take medicines called glucocorticoids or steroids for a wide range of diseases, you are at an especially high risk for osteoporosis. Talk to your doctor about alternative medications or therapies.

2. If you take an osteoporosis medication, be sure to follow the prescription to the letter. Take all recommended doses at the right times.

3. Your age, ethnicity, weight, hormone levels and medications can put you at increased risk for osteoporosis. Log on to www.speakingofwomenshealth.com for a list of increased risk factors.

4. Osteopenia refers to bone mineral density that is lower than normal, but not low enough to be classified as osteoporosis. Having osteopenia means that there is a greater risk that you may develop bone mineral density that is very low compared to normal, causing osteoporosis.

If you are diagnosed with osteoporosis, ask your health care provider about the range of treatment options. Along with lifestyle changes, there may be medications that could be a part of your therapy.

These include bisphosphonates, calcitonin, selective estrogen receptor modulators, anabolic therapy and estrogen/hormone replacement therapy.

Recipe from Kelli Freeman, *Director of 7UP Brand Marketing,*
Cadbury Schweppes Americas Beverages

Christmas Day Green Chili Casserole

This Green Chili Casserole is anything but ho-ho-hum! Serve this up and your family will say, "Yum! Yum! Yum!"

INGREDIENTS

6 large	Anaheim peppers
2 Tbsp.	canola oil
1 lb.	chicken breasts, diced boned and defatted
2 cups	diced red onion
2 tsp.	garlic, minced
1 tsp.	dried oregano
6 Tbsp.	all-purpose flour
1 qt.	low-sodium chicken stock
1 Tbsp.	lime juice
6 Tbsp.	cornstarch
6 Tbsp.	low-sodium chicken stock
1/2 cup	half and half
1 1/2 tsp.	salt
18	corn tortillas
12 oz.	shredded cheddar cheese

NUTRITIONAL ANALYSIS
Makes 8 servings. Each serving contains approximately:

385	calories
30 g.	protein
41 g.	carbohydrates
12 g.	fat
54 mg.	cholesterol
684 mg.	sodium
5 g.	fiber

PREPARATION

- Preheat oven to 350 degrees.
- On a baking sheet place peppers in oven and roast for 45 minutes. Cool. Peel peppers and remove stems and seeds. Dice peppers and set aside.
- In a large saucepot, sauté diced chicken with canola oil until almost cooked through. Add onions and garlic and sauté until onions are translucent. Add roasted peppers and oregano and sauté briefly. Add flour and cook for 3 minutes. Add first amount of chicken stock and lime juice and bring to a boil. Reduce heat to a simmer and cook for 10 minutes.
- In a small bowl, combine cornstarch and second amount of chicken stock and mix. Add cornstarch mixture to chicken mixture and cook for 2 minutes. Remove from heat and stir in half and half and salt.
- In a 9"x13" casserole dish, lay 6 tortillas on the bottom. Pour 1/2 of the chicken mixture over tortillas and cover with 1/2 of the cheese. Repeat, ending with cheese. Bake for 45 minutes.

"Excellence is doing the best against all odds"

Dear Mom,

"The Little Engine That Could"

Marilyn Hughes Gaston, M.D. – former Assistant Surgeon General

You

left us too soon before I was mature and experienced enough to really thank you for your gifts of love. I thank you from the bottom of my heart for:

- Bestowing on me the names of fierce women as lifelong role models to support me – Marilyn (after Mary, the Mother of Jesus) and LuAnna (after Lula and Anna, my Grandmothers).

- Empowering me as a little girl to believe I could do and be anything I desired. Repeated readings of "The Little Engine That Could" armed me for future life challenges.

- Instilling the belief that poverty, sexism and racism were not to be seen as major impediments in my life or to be used as excuses for failure.

- Instead, instilling the belief that being a woman and "colored" was a blessing.

- Repeating your mantras – that I hated growing up and would roll my eyes whenever you threw one out – but now I find myself repeating them: "Pretty is as pretty does," "Never give up, never give out, never give in," and "All I ask is that you do the best you can."

- Teaching that "Excellence is doing your best against the odds."

- Giving my brother and me a love for learning and exploring new lands, people, foods and feelings.

- Role-modeling your Mother Bear fierceness, energy, determination, unconditional love and faith in God.

- Teaching me that the substance of life is about love, character, determination, attitude, helping others, passion and taking risks.

- Demonstrating what Kahlil Gibran said, "Work is love made visible."

- Putting into action your activism and ability to protest against unfairness – to the extent of once mounting a one-woman picket line.

- Laying the foundation for my journey as a woman, an African American, a Mother, a healer and a child of God.

- Being the kind of Mother that I couldn't wait to see, to be with, to tell all my deepest darkest secrets, to laugh and cry with.

- Giving me the gift of a relationship where my most enduring hope in life has been for you to look at me, Dorothy's Daughter, and with pride proclaim, "Well Done!"

With much love and thanks,

Marilyn

BEAUTY REST

Remember when Mom read you the story of "Sleeping Beauty"?

Well, when you are getting a good night's sleep, you don't want a prince or a frog to awaken you! When you are desperate for sleep and don't have a spinning wheel around, try some of these helpful tips in this chapter.

Getting Your ZZZZZ's

1 Establish a routine for bedtime. Not only does this allow you to relax and unwind, but also sends a signal to your brain that it's time to sleep.

2 Avoid caffeine, nicotine and alcohol in the evening. Caffeine and nicotine can delay your sleep and alcohol may interrupt sleep later in the night.

3 Exercise regularly, but at least 3 hours before bedtime. A workout close to bedtime may keep you awake because your body hasn't had a chance to cool down. If you must exercise in the evening, consider Yoga or end your workout with quiet mediation to calm and restore you.

4 If you have trouble sleeping when you go to bed, don't nap during the day.

5 Consider your sleep environment. Make it as pleasant, comfortable, dark and quiet as possible. Remove distractions or stressors such as files from work or bills. Create an environment that is inviting and calming.

6 Avoid exposure to bright light just before bedtime. Consider a warm bath to help calm yourself.

7 Try to clear your mind. This is not the time to rethink the day's problems or plan tomorrow's to-do list.

8 If sleep problems persist for more than a week or if sleepiness interferes with daily routine, talk to your health care provider. Consider keeping a diary of activities before bedtime, detailing sleep/awake times and steps you have taken that have not worked.

Why a Good Night's Sleep is Important

Just as food, water and oxygen are essential to sustain life, sleep is required to allow the body and mind time to rest and restore energy.

1. Many clinical studies confirm that a lack of sleep weakens the immune system, leaving you susceptible to diabetes, cancers and even the common cold.

2. A lack of sleep increases stress, which also weakens your immune defenses.

3. A lack of sleep can also lead to confusion, memory problems and may increase the likelihood of loss of balance and falls for older adults.

4. Reducing your nighttime sleep by as little as one and a half hours for just one night could result in a reduction of daytime alertness by as much as 32%.

5. Excessive sleepiness also contributes to a greater than two-fold higher risk of sustaining an injury while at work and increases the likelihood of an automobile accident.

The good news is...
help is available. More than 85 different types of sleep disorders have been recognized by the medical community. There's no reason to lose another wink.

Fruit Muffins

Get a great start to the day for the entire family. Consider making these muffins on Sunday morning... make enough to freeze and pop out for a mid-week treat.

INGREDIENTS

1 cup	all-purpose flour
1/2 cup	whole-wheat pastry flour
2 tsp.	baking powder
1/2 tsp.	salt
1	whole egg
1/3 cup	2% milk
1/3 cup	non-fat plain yogurt
2 Tbsp.	canola oil
1/3 cup	sugar
1 cup	peeled and chopped fruit or fresh berries

Topping

pinch	cinnamon
2 Tbsp.	sugar

Optional

1/4 cup	walnut pieces

NUTRITIONAL ANALYSIS
Makes 12 muffins. Each muffin without walnuts contains approximately:

135	calories
3 g.	protein
24 g.	carbohydrates
3 g.	fat
15 mg.	cholesterol
87 mg.	sodium
2 g.	fiber

PREPARATION

- Preheat oven to 350 degrees.
- Lightly coat cups of a 12-cup muffin tin with canola oil.
- In large bowl, combine flours, baking powder and salt.
- In a medium bowl, combine egg, milk, yogurt and oil. Add sugar and mix well.
- Pour egg mixture into dry ingredients and stir until all ingredients are moistened. Add fruit and stir until just mixed.
- Fill each muffin cup with 1/4 cup batter, sprinkle each with optional walnut pieces, then bake for 15 to 20 minutes or until muffins are golden and toothpick inserted into center comes out clean.
- To prepare topping, mix together cinnamon and sugar. Sprinkle 1/2 tsp. over each warm muffin. Cool and remove from tins.

Cook's Notes

Try popular fruit combinations such as apple-cranberry, peach-apricot and blueberry-lemon in this recipe. Spices such as cinnamon and cardamon can add variety as well as vanilla, almond and orange extract. Or, try adding a tsp. of grated orange, lemon or lime peel.

Unconditional LOVE!

Dear Mom,

I want to thank you for the love and support you have given me in my life. For all of the times you went without so I could have. For believing I could do anything I put my mind to... and telling me that when I needed to hear it most. For always focusing on the positive no matter how bad the situation was. For loving me unconditionally even when I was difficult. For making me laugh until I cried and for being such a wonderful Grandmother to my children.

I would never be who I am or what I am without you.

I love you!!!

Lisa

COLDS & ALLERGIES

Colds

1 The best way to treat a cold is to prevent it from happening! Keep an instant hand sanitizer "on hand" to kill germs. In addition, drink plenty of fluids and consider boosting your immune system with vitamins.

2 Remember what Mom taught you... with a new *twist!* DO cover your mouth and nose when coughing or sneezing to avoid transmitting germs to others. BUT... DON'T use your hands to cover. The new thinking is to cough or sneeze into the crook, or V, of your elbow. This helps keep germs away from hands and the surfaces they come into contact with.

3 Contrary to popular belief, you won't catch a cold from exposure to cold weather. Although colds are most common in the autumn and winter months, they result from a virus, which spreads from one person to another through close contact.

4 Persistent colds may be a sign of sinusitis, or sinus infection. More than 37 million Americans suffer from sinus infections every year. Allergic reactions and infections can clog your sinus passageways, causing pressure and creating a long-lasting infection.

5 While sinusitis can be difficult to distinguish from colds, treatment is available. Any cold that lingers more than a week or is accompanied by a fever warrants a call to your doctor.

6 When choosing medicines for colds and/or allergies, you should always start with those less likely to have side effects. Some are formulated for day (non-drowsy) or nighttime (may cause drowsiness). Follow dosages and instructions on the box, and speak to your pharmacist if you are taking other medications to avoid potentially-dangerous drug interactions.

Allergies

1 An allergy is an over-reaction of your body's immune system. It's caused when the immune system reacts to things that are usually harmless. It produces antibodies that cause the body's cells to produce histamine, which creates the allergic reaction.

2 To avoid allergy symptoms, you must avoid contact with what triggers them. If you're going into a place that is known to trigger your allergies (household with cats, outside into air with high pollen count, etc.), consider taking medication ahead of time.

3 While most allergic reactions are mild, others can be quite severe. An asthma attack is a severe reaction to something that has been breathed into the lungs of a person susceptible to that antigen. Anaphylaxis is another severe reaction that can occur within minutes of being exposed to a trigger like peanuts. Symptoms can include difficulty breathing and swallowing, swelling of the lips, throat and tongue, dizziness and possible loss of consciousness. Call 9-1-1 immediately should any of these symptoms arise.

4 Allergies can be grouped by the nature of their symptoms. These include respiratory or seasonal allergies that cause runny nose, itchy or watery eyes; skin allergies that bring out hives or rash; and food allergies that may cause swelling and difficulty breathing.

5 Some of the most common allergic reactions come from foods, insect stings, medicines, chemicals and airborne antigens like pollen, grasses, animal dander, dust mites, dust and mold.

6 If you are allergic to dust mites, cover your pillows and mattresses with an impermeable cover and wash sheets and blankets weekly in the hottest water they can stand.

7 If you are allergic to cats or dogs, you are allergic to the saliva, urine or dander. Keep the pet out of your bedroom and house, when possible.

8 A person usually does not inherit one specific allergy from their parents – rather the probability of having allergies, in general.

Colds & Allergies: What's the Connection?

Allergies can severely weaken your immune system, making you more susceptible to colds and flu.

Eggplant Parmesan

You don't have to speak Italian to say "deliciouso!" to this classic favorite. Add a lovely green salad to complete this meal... and perhaps a piece of dark chocolate for dessert.

INGREDIENTS

Eggplant Parmesan

1	eggplant, about 1/2 lb.
1	egg
3 1/2 Tbsp.	2% milk
1/2 cup	all-purpose flour
1/4 cup	breadcrumbs
1 Tbsp.	olive oil
3/4 cup	marinara sauce, see recipe
1/2 cup	low-fat mozzarella cheese, shredded
1 Tbsp.	Parmesan cheese, grated
1 1/3 cups	cooked angel hair pasta
2 cups	cooked broccolini

Marinara Sauce

1 cup	onion, chopped
1 Tbsp.	garlic, minced
1/2 Tbsp.	fresh oregano, finely chopped
1/2 Tbsp.	fresh basil, finely chopped
1/2 tsp.	ground dried thyme
1/2 tsp.	ground coarse black pepper
1/4 tsp.	red chili pepper flakes
1 tsp.	olive oil
6 1/4 cups	canned diced tomatoes
3/4 cup	vegetable stock
1	bay leaf
2 tsp.	parsley, freshly chopped

PREPARATION

Eggplant Parmesan

- Preheat oven to 400 degrees.
- Cut eggplant into 8 slices, each slice 1/4-inch thick.
- In a small bowl, beat egg with milk. Dredge eggplant slices in flour, then in egg milk mixture, then in breadcrumbs.
- In a large sauté pan, sauté eggplant in olive oil over medium-high heat for 3-5 minutes on each side.
- Transfer cooked eggplant slices to a baking dish. Top with marinara sauce and sprinkle cheeses over the top. Place in oven and cook for a few minutes until cheese is melted and bubbly.
- Serve 2 eggplant slices with 1/3 cup cooked pasta and 1/2 cup cooked broccolini.

Marinara Sauce

- In a large sauce pan, sauté onion, garlic, oregano, basil, thyme, black pepper and red pepper flakes in olive oil until onions are soft. Add diced tomatoes and bring to a simmer.
- Add remaining ingredients except for parsley and bring to a boil. Reduce heat and simmer for 1 1/2 to 2 hours stirring frequently. Stir in parsley.

NUTRITIONAL ANALYSIS Makes 4 servings.
Each serving (1/3 cup) contains approximately:

380	calories
15 g.	protein
56 g.	carbohydrates
10 g.	fat
63 mg.	cholesterol
310 mg.	sodium
6 g.	fiber

Who knew where she would go?

Dear

Mom, Dad and Phoebe on top of the world... or at least on top of the Alps!

Three generations of love

Mom,

It is with great admiration that I write you this letter filled with thoughts of our Mother-Daughter experiences. Until recently, when I became a Mother, I could not imagine the joy and pain of raising children. The ink could fill volumes of pages but some moments capture these memories with such freshness I can still taste them.

I think back to funny times like when I was 10 years old and we were sitting at the kitchen table belly laughing because my appetite was so big I ate an entire chicken, and then I asked for more. I think about the growing pains of wanting to grow up before I was ready and you trying every which way to tell me, "Not so fast." Those years seemed to stretch on longer than they should have. Sometimes I am a slow learner. Then, sometimes in life, as in mine, something happens that changes everything. I know you still relive my spinal cord injury, much more than I, even though 19 years have passed. And while you remember the pain of seeing me paralyzed from the shoulders down and wondering what kind of a future I would have, I remember your determined smile and the strength in you like a Mother who lifts a car when her child is beneath it. You were resolved – I was going to walk out of my rehabilitation hospital, even if the odds were stacked high against me. You know what? I did! It never occurred to me that I wouldn't walk right out the front door and into the rest of my very bright future.

I never knew how hard it must have been to face such fear until I had children of my own. Now I understand. If Mothers can lift cars, then we can surely make lemonade. Life is a rich garden, with sweet apples and hot peppers and when the lemons we grow are too sour, with a little magic, we make lemonade. Mom, you have taught me to sweeten life when the knocks are hard and the taste is tart. I am lucky to have you, as are my children.

You continue to show us every day how to carve our own paths while taking an active role in our community. Your work to educate women about healthy living inspires us to live healthfully both within ourselves and within our community. Of all of the things you do so beautifully, the best is being a loving Mother to me and an adoring Grandmother to my children.

With Much Love,

Phoebe

SELF ESTEEM

Our self-esteem is influenced not only by our Moms...

...but also by our Grandmothers, our Aunts, and all of the wonderful women who we look up to and admire. It's safe to say that this is not a case of "either/or." Self-esteem comes from nature and nurture. Knowing ourselves and choosing to hear the "positives" can give us a life filled with self-confidence, a sense of humor and the wish to be our best.

Understanding Self-Esteem

As Louise Hart, a psychologist and educator, wrote, "Self-esteem creates natural highs. Knowing that you're lovable helps you to love more. Knowing that you're important helps you to make a difference to others. Knowing that you are capable empowers you to create more. Knowing that you're valuable and that you have a special place in the universe is a serene spiritual joy in itself."

1   Self-esteem is our birthright. Acknowledge and celebrate the self-esteem that you have.

2   First and foremost, begin with self-love. It's OK to toot your own horn a bit – this isn't selfish, but more of a self-fulfilling act of appreciation. When you like who you are, you can effectively share your wholesome self with others.

Boosting Your Self-Esteem

1   Be sincere, up front and true to who you are. You are valuable and your opinion does matter, so don't mask your true feelings. If someone doesn't know the real you, they can never love you for who you really are.

2   Find time to nourish yourself physically, psychologically, emotionally and spiritually. This cultivates a positive self-esteem mindset.

3   Surround yourself with positive people to boost your self-esteem.

4   Instead of focusing on the things you cannot do, make a list every day of the accomplishments that you've made throughout that day. Whether it was landing that big deal or making a home-cooked meal for your family, you are using your talents to the best of your ability and setting a good example for others.

5 Learn about what can hurt self-esteem and what can build it.

6 Don't ignore, but explore your differences with others in your life. Celebrate your differences by forming healthy relationships and really getting to know and respect each other's opinions.

7 If it doesn't fit, don't force it. Don't force yourself to put up with any condition or any person that causes you discomfort.

8 Break old patterns of unhealthy relationships. Make it a priority to empty out all emotional baggage from the past to increase your self-esteem and form healthy, lasting relationships.

9 Let people know how to change their behavior in positive, caring ways. This helps boost their self-esteem and rejuvenate positive thinking about themselves.

10 Think about how you can share your special talents with others. If you are a great artist, consider donating your services to a local nonprofit to design something for a fundraiser. If you exercise, consider registering for a walk to combat a disease in your community.

11 Consider helping others, like raising money for a cause you believe in. Once you start thinking about other people, you won't be so focused on your problems.

12 Surround yourself with friends who love you for who you are, not what you wear, the job you have, the education you have or how you look.

Boosting Your Family's Self-Esteem

1 Take time to think about the words you use, how you say them and their impact on others.

2 Encourage children in your life to claim that they are lovable and capable in order to cultivate good self-esteem.

3 Let your children know that they do not have to be involved in relationships with people who are disrespectful and hurt their self-esteem.

4 Establish clear rules and guidelines based on family values.

5 Explore a variety of ways to offer family members messages that convey unconditional love, as well as appreciation for what they do.

6 Make sure that the positive messages you offer to others are sincere.

Rainy Day Smoothie

Turn a damp, rainy day into something really fun for the kids and you to enjoy... a healthy smoothie and a filling nutritious snack will put the sunshine into their hearts and spirits!

INGREDIENTS

1	mango, peeled, seeded and cut into chunks
1	banana, peeled and chopped
1 cup	fresh orange juice
1 cup	vanilla non-fat yogurt

PREPARATION

- Place mango, banana, orange juice and yogurt in a blender.
- Blend until smooth. Serve in clear glass.

NUTRITIONAL ANALYSIS
Makes 4 servings. Each serving contains approximately:

120	calories
4 g.	protein
27 g.	carbohydrates
1 mg.	cholesterol
42 mg.	sodium
3 g.	fiber
	trace fat

Index

Index

OUR HOSPITAL PARTNERS*

Speaking of Women's Health is proud to partner with these hospitals to provide the latest, most up-to-date educational resources and information. As part of our mission to "educate women to make informed decisions about their health, well-being and personal safety," we have partnered with these health care institutions because we feel they have shared goals and a common vision with us.

St. Anthony Medical Center, Crown Point, IN

Sarasota Memorial Health Care System, Sarasota, FL

The Women's Pavilion at St. Mark's Hospital, Salt Lake City, UT

Baptist Health, Jacksonville, FL

Tampa General Hospital, Tampa Bay, FL

St. Vincent Women's Hospital, Indianapolis, IN

Washington Regional Medical Center, Northwest AR

Shawnee Mission Medical Center, Kansas City, KS

Northwestern Memorial Hospital, Chicago, IL

WellStar Health System, Atlanta, GA

WakeMed Health & Hospitals, Raleigh, NC

Strong Health, Rochester, NY

Miami Valley Hospital, Dayton, OH

Cleveland Clinic Florida, Miami, FL

Virginia Commonwealth University Institute for Women's Health, Richmond, VA

TriHealth Women's Health: Bethesda North and Good Samaritan Hospitals, Cincinnati, OH

Boone Hospital, Columbia, MO

The Cleveland Clinic Foundation, Cleveland, OH

Sara Lee Center for Women's Health at Forsyth Medical Center, Winston-Salem, NC

King's Daughters' Hospital, Madison, IN

Margaret Mary Community Hospital, Batesville, IN

Covenant Health Systems, Waterloo, IA

Northwest Texas Healthcare System, Amarillo, TX

Orlando Regional Healthcare, Orlando, FL

Sharpe Health Care System, San Diego, CA

Mercy Health Partners, Cincinnati, OH

Jackson Hospital, Montgomery, AL

Mills-Peninsula Health Services, San Mateo, CA

*as of this printing

Speaking of Women's Health's "Love Notes to Our Moms and Other Women of Influence" is meant to increase your knowledge of current developments in women's health. In no way, however, are any of the suggestions in this book meant to take the place of advice given by your licensed health care professionals. Consult your physician or other licensed health care professional before commencing any medical treatment or exercise program. Speaking of Women's Health doesn't make any claims or endorsements for any products, services or procedures that appear in this book.